WALKING WITH SPIRITS

Native American Myths, Legends, And Folklore

Written and Edited by
G.W. Mullins
With Original Art by
C.L. Hause

LIGHT OF THE MOON PUBLISHING

ISBN 978-1-64570-952-7

Revised Second Edition Printing

Light Of The Moon Publishing has allowed this work to remain exactly as the author intended, verbatim, without editorial input.

Printed in the United States of America

The following book represents a collection of Native American works which are public domain. You may have read the stories before. In true story telling fashion, the stories have been left as close to the original form as possible. In Native American culture, in order to pass the stories along with all information intact, they had to be told pretty much word for word, to keep the legends alive. Many of these stories were translated directly from original Native language texts. With that in mind, please be aware that some spellings and word usage may vary from one tribe to another. For instance, the spelling of "teepee", as used in this book, can also be written as "tipi", and "tepee". All are correct. Also, when using words like "someone", in most native cultures, it would be "some one". So, keep in mind, these are not necessarily misspellings. They are simply dialect and translations.

<u>**Other Titles Available From G.W. Mullins And C.L. Hause**</u>
Walking With Spirits Native American Myths, Legends, And Folklore
Volumes One Thru Six

The Native American Cookbook

Native American Cooking - An Indian Cookbook With Legends And Folklore

The Native American Story Book - Stories Of The American Indians For Children
Volumes One Thru Five

The Best Native American Stories For Children

Cherokee A Collection of American Indian Legends, Stories And Fables

Creation Myths - Tales Of The Native American Indians

Strange Tales Of The Native American Indians

Spirit Quest - Stories Of The Native American Indians

Animal Tales Of The Native American Indians

Medicine Man - Shamanism, Natural Healing, Remedies And Stories Of The Native
American Indians

Native American Legends: Stories Of The Hopi Indians
Volumes One and Two

Totem Animals Of The Native Americans

The Best Native American Myths, Legends And Folklore
Volumes One Thru Three

Ghosts, Spirits And The Afterlife In Native American Indian Mythology And Folklore

The Native American Art Book – Art Inspired By Native American Myths And Legends

For information about the book and novel releases of
G.W. Mullins please visit his web site at *http://gwmullins.wix.com/books*

All images contained in this book are original works by
C.L. Hause. For more information on his art and other projects please visit his
web page at *http://clarencehause.wix.com/homepage*

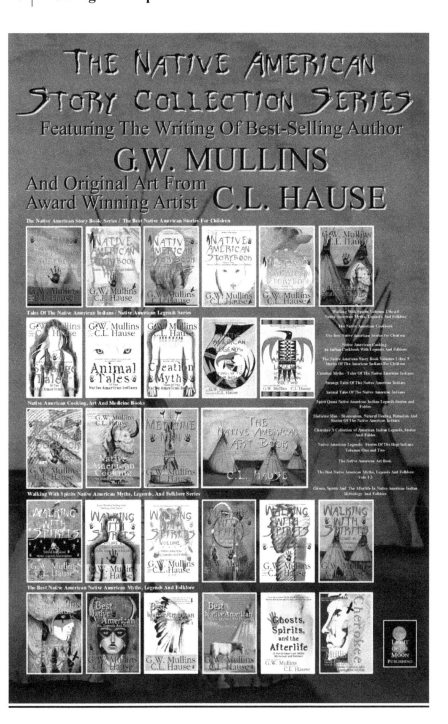

This book is dedicated to Vince Mullins, my Grandfather (Pawpaw). He was a tall red man with a fire in his eyes. He filled my childhood with laughter and love. This book has reminded me how much I miss his stories. - G.W. Mullins

This book is also dedicated to Chief Dan George. We could all learn so much from his wisdom and humanity.

**"May the stars carry your sadness away,
May the flowers fill your heart with beauty,
May hope forever wipe away your tears,
And, above all, may silence make you strong."**

~ Chief Dan George

Chief Dan George, (July 24, 1899 – September 23, 1981) was a chief of the Tsleil-Waututh Nation, a Coast Salish band located on Burrard Inlet in North Vancouver, British Columbia, Canada. He was also an author, poet, actor, and an Officer of the Order of Canada. At the age of 71, he was nominated for an Academy Award for Best Supporting Actor in Little Big Man.

Anywhere is the Center of the World
Black Elk (Holy Man of the Oglala Sioux)

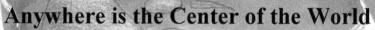

Then I was standing on the highest mountain of them all, and round about beneath me was the whole hoop of the world. And while I stood there I saw more than I can tell and I understood more than I saw; for I was seeing in a sacred manner the shapes of all things in the spirit, and the shape of all shapes as they must live together like one being.

And I say the sacred hoop of my people was one of the many hoops that made one circle, wide as daylight and as starlight, and in the center grew one mighty flowering tree to shelter all the children of one mother and one father. And I saw that it was holy...

But anywhere is the center of the world.

Native American Blessing

Above you are the stars, below you are the stones.
As time does pass, remember:
Like a star should your love be constant.
Like a stone should your love be firm.
Be close, yet not too close.
Possess one another, yet be understanding.
Have patience with the other; for storms will come, but they will
go quickly.
Be free in giving of affection and warmth.
Make love often, and be sensuous to one another.
Have no fear, and let not the ways of words of the
unenlightened give you unease.
For the Great Spirit is with you, now and always.

Table Of Contents

Introduction

Before the time of books, computers, tablets and recording devices, the history of many cultures was passed down, from person to person, by word of mouth. The rich histories of so many people were told in songs, chants, poems and stories. This was and still is the way of Native American tribes. Each in its own way enriching their stories with their own experiences. By reliving these stories and songs, we have the opportunity to bring life back to the ancient spirits that created them. We have a chance to walk with the spirits of the past.

Native Americans used their stories to teach the children the traditions of their grandfathers. It was in this way that local customs were passed down and lessons were taught about how to live off the land and track animals. It was with stories they learned to grow crops and thrive in their natural environment.

When foreign men entered and settled upon Indian sacred lands, the Native Americans were often forcibly removed. They were sent to areas unfamiliar. If it were not for their customs, language and tradition passed down through stories, they would have lost connection with who they were. These songs and myths were their way of keeping their legacy alive.

Today Native Americans still keep their tribal languages alive. The myths, and legends are still passed down from generation to generation.

Mythology

Mythology has always played a huge role in Native American stories. Of the stories told, those of Creation are often best known. Nature has always been looked at as an unfolding mystery. And in the stories of Native Americans, they sought to explain everything from natural occurrences, to animals, plant life, and weather related events. It was a way to express their ideas of their own beginnings.

Among all the stories told, each tribe had their own views of creation and how life came into this world. While some themes were similar, others could not be more different. In their stories, they explored the importance of Native American culture but also the individuality of each tribe and it's believes. These myths pay respect to the ancient ones that came before them and how nature has shaped their lives.

Songs, Poems and Music

Story telling didn't just involve words, or simple retelling of history. It included chants, poems, songs and music. Much set to the sound of a drum. The drumming invited everyone into the dance. After all, these stories and history were meant to be shared by all. It has been and still is custom to share stories and music at pow-wows.

Legacy

Through storytelling, the rich history of the Native American tribes is alive and well today. It has been shared and preserved and still pays tribute to fallen heroes of the past. Often, Native Americans have been misrepresented as violent people. It is through the glimpses into the past, and these stories much like the ones that are contained in this book, that you can see what a proud heritage they possess and how in tune with the Earth Native Americans really are.

Being there were so many different tribes with countless beliefs and customs, the only way to understand their ways is through understanding their stories. In this book I have endeavored to show a wide landscape of different tribes and hopefully present a true look at their beliefs.

With this book I hope you understand the Native American people a little better and understand where they have come from and what they can offer the world. By exploring these stories I offer you a glimpse into an often forgotten past. The past of my people. I was born Cherokee and as a child heard many of these stories. These stories were passed to me in the old traditional way by my grandfather. And now I give these stories to you, to carry forward for younger generations to explore and learn.

I invite you to go Walking With Spirits.

Grandfather Great Spirit

All over the world the faces
of living ones are alike.

With tenderness they have
come up out of the ground.

Look upon your children
that they may face the winds
And walk the good road to the Day of Quiet.

Grandfather Great Spirit
Fill us with the Light.
Give us the strength to understand,
And the eyes to see.

Teach us to walk the soft Earth
as relatives to all that live.

Origin of the Pleiades
(An Onondaga Legend)

A long time ago a party of Indians went through the woods toward a good hunting-ground, which they had long known. They traveled several days through a very wild country, going on leisurely and camping by the way.

At last they reached Kan-ya-ti-yo, "the beautiful lake," where the gray rocks were crowned with great forest trees. Fish swarmed in the waters, and at every jutting point the deer came down from the hills around to bathe or drink of the lake. On the hills and in the valleys were huge beech and chestnut trees, where squirrels chattered, and bears came to take their morning and evening meals.

The chief of the band was Hah-yah-no, "Tracks in the water," and he halted his party on the lake shore that he might return thanks to the Great Spirit for their safe arrival at this good hunting-ground. "Here will we build our lodges for the winter, and may the Great Spirit, who has prospered us on our way, send us plenty of game, and health and peace." The Indian is always thankful.

The pleasant autumn days passed on. The lodges had been built, and hunting had prospered, when the children took a fancy to dance for their own amusement. They were getting lonesome, having little to do, and so they met daily in a quiet spot by the lake to have what they called their jolly dance. They had done this a long time, when one day a very old man came to them. They had seen no one like him before. He was dressed in white feathers, and his white hair shone like silver. His appearance was strange, his words were unpleasant as well. He told them they must stop their dancing, or evil would happen to them. Little did the children heed, for they were intent on their sport, and again and again the old man appeared, repeating his warning.

The mere dances did not afford all the enjoyment the children wished, and a little boy, who liked a good dinner, suggested a feast the next time they met. The food must come from their parents, and all were asked when they returned home. "You will waste and spoil good victuals," said one. "You can eat at home as you should," said another, and so they got nothing at all. Sorry as they were for this, they met and danced as before. A little to eat after each dance would have made them happy indeed. Empty stomachs cause no joy.

One day, as they danced, they found themselves rising little by little into the air, their heads being light through hunger. How this happened they did not know, but one said, "Do not look back, for something strange is taking place." A woman, saw them rise, and called them back, but with no effect, for they still rose slowly above the earth. She ran to the camp, and all rushed out with food of every kind, but the children would not return, though their parents called piteously after them. When one would look back he became a falling star. The others reached the sky, and are now what we call the Pleiades, and the Onondagas Oot-kwa-tah. Every falling or shooting star recalls the story, but the seven stars shine on continuously, a pretty band of dancing children.

Only when the last tree has died
and the last river been poisoned and the last fish been caught
will we realize we cannot eat money.
~ Cree Indian Proverb ~

The Woman Who Fell from the Sky
(Seneca)

from Stith Thompson, *Tales of the North American Indians* (1929)

A long time ago human beings lived high up in what is now called heaven. They had a great and illustrious chief.

It so happened that this chief's daughter was taken very ill with some strange affliction. Every known remedy was tried in an attempt to cure her, but none had any effect.

Near the lodge of this chief stood a great tree, which every year bore corn used for food. One of the friends of the chief had a dream in which he was advised to tell the chief that, in order to cure his daughter, he must lay her beside this tree, and that he must have the tree dug up. This advice was carried out to the letter. While the people were at work and the young woman lay there, a young man came along. He was very angry and said: "It is not at all right to destroy this tree. Its fruit is all that we have to live on." With this remark he gave the young woman who lay there ill a shove with his foot, causing her to fall into the hole that had been dug.

Now, that hole opened into this world, which was then all water, on which floated waterfowl of many kinds. There was no land at that time. It came to pass that as these waterfowl saw this young woman falling they shouted, "Let us receive her," whereupon they, at least some of them, joined their bodies together, and the young woman fell on this platform of bodies. When these were wearied they asked, "Who will volunteer to care for this woman?" The great Turtle then took her, and when he got tired of holding her, he in turn asked who would take his place. At last the question arose as to what they should do to provide her with a permanent resting place in this world. Finally it was decided to prepare the earth, on which she would live in the future. To do this it was determined that soil from the bottom of the primal sea should be brought up and placed on the broad, firm carapace of the Turtle, where it would increase in size to such an extent that it would accommodate all the creatures that should be produced thereafter. After much discussion the toad was finally persuaded to dive to the bottom of the waters in search of soil. Bravely making the attempt, he succeeded in bringing up soil from the depths of the sea. This was carefully spread over the carapace of the Turtle, and at once both began to grow in size and depth.

After the young woman recovered from the illness from which she suffered when she was cast down from the upper world, she built herself a shelter, in which she lived quite contentedly. In the course of time she brought forth a girl baby, who grew rapidly in size and intelligence.

When the daughter had grown to young womanhood, the mother and she were accustomed to go out to dig wild potatoes. Her mother had said to her that in doing this she must face the west at all times. Before long the young daughter gave signs that she was about to become a mother. Her mother reproved her, saying that she had violated the injunction not to face the east, as her condition showed that she had faced the wrong way while digging potatoes. It is said that the breath of the West Wind had entered her person, causing conception. When the days of her delivery were at hand, she overheard twins within her body in a hot debate as to which should be born first and as to the proper place of exit, one declaring that he was going to emerge through the armpit of his mother, the other saying that he would emerge in the natural way. The first one born, who was of a reddish color, was called

Othagwenda, that is, Flint. The other, who was light in color, was called Djuskaha, that is, the Little Sprout.

The grandmother of the twins liked Djuskaha [Little Sprout] and hated the other, so they cast Othagwenda [Flint] into a hollow tree some distance from the lodge.

The boy who remained in the lodge grew very rapidly, and soon was able to make himself bows and arrows and to go out to hunt in the vicinity. Finally, for several days he returned home without his bow and arrows. At last he was asked why he had to have a new bow and arrows every morning. He replied that there was a young boy in a hollow tree in the area who used them. The grandmother inquired where the tree stood, and he told her; whereupon then they went there and brought the other boy home again.

When the boys had grown to man's estate, they decided that it was necessary for them to increase the size of their island, so they agreed to start out together, afterward separating to create forests and lakes and other things. They parted as agreed, Othagwenda [Flint] going westward and Djuskaha [Little Sprout] eastward. In the course of time, on returning they met in their shelter or lodge at night, then agreeing to go the next day to see what each had made. First they went west to see what Othagwenda [Flint] had made. It was found that he had made the country all rocks and full of ledges, and also a mosquito that was very large. Djuskaha asked the mosquito to run, in order that he might see whether the insect could fight. The mosquito ran, and sticking his bill through a sapling, thereby made it fall, at which Djuskaha [Little Sprout] said, "That will not be right, for you would kill the people who are about to come." So, seizing him, he rubbed him down in his hands, causing him to become very small; then he blew on the mosquito, whereupon he flew away. He also modified some of the other animals that his brother had made. After returning to their lodge, they agreed to go the next day to see what Djuskaha [Little Sprout] had fashioned.

On visiting the east the next day, they found that Djuskaha had made a large number of animals which were so fat that they could hardly move; that he had made the sugar-maple trees to drop syrup; that he had made the sycamore tree to bear fine fruit; that the rivers were so formed that half the water flowed upstream and the other half downstream. Then the reddish-colored brother, Othagwenda [Flint], was greatly displeased with what his brother had made, saying that the people who were about to come would live too easily and be too happy. So he shook violently the various animals--the bears, deer, and turkeys--causing them to become small at once, a characteristic that attached itself to their descendants. He also caused the sugar maple to drop sweetened water only, and the fruit of the sycamore to become small and useless; and lastly he caused the water of the rivers to flow in only one direction, because the original plan would make it too easy for the human beings who were about to come to navigate the streams.

The inspection of each other's work resulted in a deadly disagreement between the brothers, who finally came to grips and blows, and Othagwenda [Flint] was killed in the fierce struggle.

I do not think the measure of a civilization
is how tall its buildings of concrete are,
But rather how well its people have learned to relate
to their environment and fellow man.
~ Sun Bear of the Chippewa Tribe ~

The Jicarilla Genesis
(Jicarilla Apache)

from James Mooney, *American Anthropologist,* Vol. XI., No. 7, Washington, D.C., July, 1898, pp. 197-209.

In the beginning the earth was covered with water, and all living things were below in the underworld. Then people could talk, the animals could talk, the trees could talk, and the rocks could talk.

It was dark in the underworld, and they used eagle plumes for torches. The people and the animals that go about by day wanted more light, but the night animals -- the Bear, the Panther, and the Owl -- wanted darkness. They disputed long, and at last agreed to play the *käyoñ'ti* game to decide the matter. It was agreed that if the day animals won there should be light, but if the night animals won it should be always dark.

The game began, but the Magpie and the Quail, which love the light and have sharp eyes, watched until they could see the button through the thin wood of the hollow stick, and they told the people under which one it was. They played once, and the people won. The morning star came out and the Black-bear ran and hid in the darkness. They played again, and the people won. It grew bright in the east and the Brown-bear ran and hid himself in a dark place. They played a third time, and the people won. It grew brighter in the east and the Mountain-lion slunk away into the darkness. They played a fourth time, and again the people won. The Sun came up in the east, and it was day, and the Owl flew away and hid himself.

Still the people were below and did not see many things, but the Sun stayed higher up and saw more. The Sun looked through a hole and saw that there was another world, this earth above. He told the people and they wanted to go there; so they built four mounds by which to reach the upper world. In the east they built a mound and planted it with all kinds of fruits and berries that were black in color. In the south they built another mound and planted on it all kinds of fruits that were blue. In the west they built another mound and planted upon it fruits that were yellow; and in the north they built a mound, and on it they planted all fruits of variegated colors. . . .

The mountains had stopped growing while their tops were yet a long way from the upper world, and the people debated how they could get up to the earth. They laid feathers crosswise for a ladder, but the feathers were too weak and they broke. They made a second ladder of larger feathers, but again they were too weak. They made a third ladder, of eagle feathers, but even these were not strong enough to bear their weight. Then the Buffalo came and offered his right horn to make a ladder, three others came and offered their right horns also. The Buffalo horns were strong, and by their help the people were able to climb up through the hole to the surface of the earth; but their weight bent the Buffalo horns, which before were straight, so that they have been curved ever since.

When the people had come up from under the earth they fastened the Sun and Moon with spider threads, so that they could not get away, and sent them up into the sky to give light. But water covered the whole earth, so four Storms went to roll the waters away. The Black-storm blew to the east and rolled up the waters into the eastern ocean. The Blue-storm blew to the south and rolled up the waters in that direction. The Yellow storm rolled up the waters in the west, and the Varicolored-storm went to the north and rolled up the waters there. So were formed the four oceans -- in the east, the south, the west, and the north. Having rolled up the waters, the Storms returned to where the people were waiting at the mouth of the hole.

First went out the Polecat, but the ground was still soft, and his legs sank in the black mud and remain black ever since. They sent the Tornado to bring him back, for the time was not yet. The Badger went out, but he, too, sank in the mud, and his legs were blackened, so they sent the Tornado to call him back. The Beaver went out, wading through the mud and swimming through the water. He began at once to build a dam to save the water still remaining in pools, and he did not return. The Tornado was sent after him and found him at work, and asked him why he had not come back.

"Because I wanted to save the water for the people to drink," said the Beaver.

"Good," said Tornado, and they went back together. They waited again, and then sent out the Crow to see if it was yet time. The Crow found the earth dry, and many dead frogs, fish, and reptiles lying on the ground. He began picking out their eyes, and did not return until Tornado was sent after him. The people were angry when they found he had been eating carrion, and they changed his color to black, which before was gray.

The earth was now all dry, excepting the four oceans around it and the lake in the center, where the Beaver had dammed up the waters. All the people came up. They went east until they came to the ocean; then they turned south until they came again to the ocean; then they turned west until they came again to the ocean, and then they turned north, and as they went each tribe stopped where it would. But the Jicarillas continued to circle around the place where they had come up from the underworld. Three times they went around, when the Ruler became displeased, and asked them where they wished to stop. They said, "In the middle of the earth;" so he led them to a place very near to Taos and left them there, and then the Taos Indians lived near them. . . .

While the Jicarillas were moving about they by accident left a girl behind them near the place where they had come up from the underworld. The girl's name was *Yo'lkai'- îstû'n*, the "Whitebead woman." The Sun shone upon her as she sat and she bore a boy child, and the Moon beamed upon her as she slept and she bore another boy child. The first born was stronger than the second, as the Sun is stronger than the Moon. When the boys were large enough to walk the Sun told her where to find her people, and she went to them.

The boys lived with their mother near Taos. . . .

Soon afterward the Sun sent word to the woman to send his son to him. The Moon-boy stayed at home with his mother, but the Sun-boy went and found his father at home. His father received him kindly and gave him a bow and arrows and a dress of turquoise, with turquoise bracelets and wrist guard and a necklace of turquoise beads for his neck. Then the Sun said to him, "Now you shall be called *Nayé- nayesxû'ni*, 'The destroyer-of-dangerous-things,' because I shall send you to destroy many dangerous things which annoy the people."

His father told him to go first against a great Frog which lived under the water in a lake by Taos, and sucked in everybody who came near. His breath was like sleet lightning at night, and he had sucked so many people under the water that there were very few Taos Indians remaining.

 . . . . His father gave him also a wheel of black stone, a wooden wheel of blue, another wheel of yellow stone, and a varicolored wheel of wood. He gave him likewise four fire-sticks, black, blue, yellow, and varicolored.

When the boy returned to Taos . . . [he] went down to the lake and stood on the east shore early in the morning as the Sun was coming up. The Frog put his head up from the lake and tried to suck him in, but the boy could not be moved, and the Frog dived under the water again. Then the boy threw the wheel of black stone into the center of the lake, and the water fell a little. He went around to the south shore and threw in the blue wheel, and the water fell yet a little more. He stood on the west shore and threw in the yellow wheel, and the water grew shallow and muddy. Then he went around to the north and threw in the varicolored wheel of wood, and at once the water was dried up, and he saw the Frog's house in the center of the lake, like a pueblo house, with four doors, one on each side, and a row of stepping stones from each door to the edge of the lake.

He went around to the east side of the lake, where he had stood at sunrise, and crossed over on the stepping stones to the first door. On each side of the door stood guard a Pueblo Indian who had been sucked in by the Frog. They had been put there to warn the Frog should an enemy approach; but the boy only spoke to them and they were unable to move. At the south door he found two bears on guard, sitting upon their haunches. At the west door he found two immense snakes, with heads erect and hissing, and at the north door he found two panthers. To each in turn he spoke, and they were motionless and allowed him to pass. Then he went inside the house, and there he found the Great Frog sitting in a room from which a door opened on each of the four sides. He asked the Frog where were all the people who had been sucked into the lake, but the Frog said he knew nothing about them. The boy knew this was not true, so he took out his four fire-sticks and twirled them rapidly until the room was full of thick smoke that choked the Frog, and it fell down dead. Then he told the two Pueblo guards to release their people, and they opened the four doors around the sides of the room, and all the rooms were filled with Pueblos who had been sucked under the water by the Frog. There were also a great many little frogs, the children of the Great

Frog; but they were too small to be dangerous, so the boy let them live, but told them they should never grow larger. From them came the present small frogs. The boy returned to Taos with all the people he had set free from under the water. The Pueblos were very grateful to have their friends restored to them and invited him to bring his mother and brother to Taos for anything they needed. He brought them there to visit for a while, and then went back to his father, the Sun, to see what was for him to do next. . . .

His father told him of still other dangerous things which must be exterminated before the people could go about their affairs in safety. It is a long story -- the whole lifetime story of *Náyenayesxû'ni* -- and space forbids the recital of all the adventurous details. He was sent next by his father to destroy two giant Bears that lived in a mountain west from Santa Clara and ravaged the whole country around. The Indian arrows only glanced from the bodies of the animals without harming them, but the boy's father showed him how to kill the he-bear by shooting him through the heart, which was in the palm of his right fore-foot. The she-bear was killed by a bolt of lightning darted by the Sun himself. The bodies were burnt and the two cubs were commanded to grow no larger, and bears remain of that size ever since.

There was also a rock, known as *Tsê'-nanlki'ñ*, "Rock-that-runs," which "lived" at Cieneguilla, east of the Rio Grande and southwest of Taos. The rock was alive and had a head and a mouth and used to roll after people and overtake and crush them and then swallow them. By the help of his father, the Sun, the boy shot an arrow through the rock and killed it. The rock is still there, lying on a level flat -- a black rock as large as a house, with its "face" to the west, and with a spot on the north and on the south side where the arrow went through, and red streaks running down from them where the blood ran down to the ground.

Other monsters he destroyed, until at last his father told him there was only one more left. This was a great winged fish which dwelt in a lake somewhere in the west and lived upon human hearts. It used to fly above the trails and dart down upon its victims, crushing in their breast-bone to get at the heart. The Sun gave this last work to the Moon-boy, who had stayed at home all this time to take care of his mother. The two brothers went on together until they came to the lake and waited for the great fish to fly out. When it came the Moon-boy struck it on the head and stunned it with a lightning bolt which the Sun had given him. Then as it lay motionless he shot four arrows into its heart. Cutting the body open, he lifted out the heart upon the four arrows and thrust it into the moon, and we see it there now.

When their work was done and the world was made safe, the boys said their last words to the people and started after the Sun along the trail to the west. Twelve men went with them. As they journeyed they came to twelve mountains, one after another, and inside of each mountain the brothers placed a man to wait forever until their return. They went on and on until they went into the western ocean, where they are living now in a house of turquoise under the green water.

Grandmother Spider Steals the Fire
(Choctaw)
A Story of the
Choctaw People of
Tennessee and
Mississippi

The Choctaw People say that when the People first came up out of the ground, People were encased in cocoons, their eyes closed, their limbs folded tightly to their bodies. And this was true of all People, the Bird People, the Animal People, the Insect People, and the Human People. The Great Spirit took pity on them and sent down someone to unfold their limbs, dry them off, and open their eyes. But the opened eyes saw nothing, because the world was dark, no sun, no moon, not even any stars.

All the People moved around by touch, and if they found something that didn't eat them first, they ate it raw, for they had no fire to cook it. All the People met in a great powwow, with the Animal and Bird People taking the lead, and the Human People hanging back. The Animal and Bird People decided that life was not good, but cold and miserable. A solution must be found! Someone spoke from the dark, "I have heard that the people in the East have fire." This caused a stir of wonder, "What could fire be?" There was a general discussion, and it was decided that if, as rumor had it, fire was warm and gave light, they should have it too. Another voice said, "But the people of the East are too greedy to share with us," So it was decided that the Bird and Animal People should steal what they needed, the fire!

But, who should have the honor? Grandmother Spider volunteered, "I can do it! Let me try!" But at the same time, Opossum began to speak. "I, Opossum, am a great chief of the animals. I will go to the East and since I am a great hunter, I will take the fire and hide it in the bushy hair on my tail." It was well know that Opossum had the furriest tail of all the animals, so he was selected.

When Opossum came to the East, he soon found the beautiful, red fire, jealously guarded by the people of the East. But Opossum got closer and closer until he picked up a small piece of burning wood, and stuck it in the hair of his tail, which promptly began to smoke, then flame. The people of the East said, "Look, that Opossum has stolen our fire!" They took it and put it back where it came from and drove Opossum away. Poor Opossum! Every bit of hair had burned from his tail, and to this day, opossums have no hair at all on their tails.

Once again, the powwow had to find a volunteer chief. Grandmother Spider again said, "Let me go! I can do it!" But this time a bird was elected, Buzzard. Buzzard was very proud. "I can succeed where Opossum has failed. I will fly to the East on my great wings, then hide the stolen fire in the beautiful long feathers on my head." The birds and animals still did not understand the nature of fire. So Buzzard flew to the East on his powerful wings, swooped past those defending the fire, picked up a small piece of burning ember, and hid it in his head feathers. Buzzard's head began to smoke and flame even faster! The people of the East said, "Look! Buzzard has stolen the fire!" And they took it and put it back where it came from.

Poor Buzzard! His head was now bare of feathers, red and blistered looking. And to this day, buzzards have naked heads that are bright red and blistered.

The powwow now sent Crow to look the situation over, for Crow was very clever. Crow at that time was pure white, and had the sweetest singing voice of all the birds. But he took so long standing over the fire, trying to find the perfect piece to steal that his white feathers were smoked black. And he breathed so much smoke that when he tried to sing, out came a harsh, "Caw! Caw!"

The Council said, "Opossum has failed. Buzzard and Crow have failed. Who shall we send?"

Tiny Grandmother Spider shouted with all her might, "LET ME TRY IT PLEASE!"

Though the council members thought Grandmother Spider had little chance of success, it was agreed that she should have her turn. Grandmother Spider looked then like she looks now, she had a small torso suspended by two sets of legs that turned the other way. She walked on all of her wonderful legs toward a stream where she had found clay. With those legs, she made a tiny clay container and a lid that fit perfectly with a tiny notch for air in the corner of the lid. Then she put the container on her back, spun a web all the way to the East, and walked tiptoe until she came to the fire. She was so small, the people from the East took no notice. She took a tiny piece of fire, put it in the container, and covered it with the lid. Then she walked back on tiptoe along the web until she came to the People. Since they couldn't see any fire, they said, "Grandmother Spider has failed."

"Oh no," she said, "I have the fire!" She lifted the pot from her back, and the lid from the pot, and the fire flamed up into its friend, the air. All the Birds and Animal People began to decide who would get this wonderful warmth. Bear said, "I'll take it!" but then he burned his paws on it and decided fire was not for animals, for look what happened to Opossum!

The Birds wanted no part of it, as Buzzard and Crow were still nursing their wounds. The insects thought it was pretty, but they, too, stayed far away from the fire.

Then a small voice said, "We will take it, if Grandmother Spider will help." The timid humans, whom none of the animals or birds thought much of, were volunteering!

So Grandmother Spider taught the Human People how to feed the fire sticks and wood to keep it from dying, how to keep the fire safe in a circle of stone so it couldn't escape and hurt them or their homes. While she was at it, she taught the humans about pottery made of clay and fire, and about weaving and spinning, at which Grandmother Spider was an expert.

The Choctaw remember. They made a beautiful design to decorate their homes, a picture of Grandmother Spider, two sets of legs up, two down, with a fire symbol on her back. This is so their children never forget to honor Grandmother Spider, Fire-bringer!

There is a road in the hearts of all of us, hidden and seldom
traveled, which leads to an unknown, secret place.
The old people came literally to love the soil,
and they sat or reclined on the ground with a feeling of
being close to a mothering power.
Their teepees were built upon the earth and their altars were made
of earth.
The soul was soothing, strengthening, cleansing and healing.
That is why the old Indian still sits upon the earth instead of
propping himself up and away from its life giving forces.
For him, to sit or lie upon the ground is to be able to think more
deeply and to feel more keenly. He can see more clearly into the
mysteries of life and come closer in kinship to other lives about
him.
~ Chief Luther Standing Bear ~

White Bead Woman
(Navaho)

[Changing Woman]
from *In the Beginning: A Navaho Creation Myth*, told by Frank Goldtooth and recorded by Stanley A. Fishler (1953, copyright not renewed)

The Sun said to the two War Twins, "Go to your mother and get her to go to the west to the ocean. This is so I can see my wife, White Bead Woman, from now on." The Sun had asked her himself, but White Bead Woman had said, "I will be lonesome there all by myself, and I will become homesick." This is why the Sun said to the Twins, "I will give all my things, all you want, all my possessions, if you get her to go there, I have done many things for you; now repay me for my kindness. Go tell your mother to go to the west."

This is what the Sun said to his sons. The Sun had many wives besides her, but White Bead Woman was jealous. That is why she did not want to go. The Sun was not coming to see [her] every day, but only once a week. The Twins went to see their mother, but still White Bead Woman did not want to go to the west, even then. All of the rest of the gods tried to help the Twins have their mother go to the west. Still she refused to go.

There was one man that did not know all of this excitement was taking place. This god was very strong so everyone decided to let him try to make White Bead Woman go west. The gods said, "We will have him try." This god was . . . the Black Flint or Fire God. None of the people had fire, only this [Black Flint], for he was the

Fire God. He would rub a stick that had been rubbed in some rocks and make fire. . . .

The old man was told to go and tell White Bead Woman to go west. He went to her and said, "How come all of your children tell you to go west to your husband, but you still don't want to go? Why?" He tried his best to try and make her go, but she still would not leave her home. At last he got desperate and said, "If you don't want to go to the west, all of the earth and gods shall be burned up." He got angrier and angrier and finally took his weapon out to start the fire (it was a rock torch). This fire was to start all over the world and would be so bad that even the water would catch on fire. Black God struck the two rocks together, or rather ground them, and they began to smoke. After he had done this only twice, the woman stopped him.

If he had done this for four times, everything on earth would have burned up. After this she started to cry and put her arms around the old man and said she would go to the west forever. White Bead Woman gathered all of her property in a white bead basket and prayed to Supreme Sacred Wind for all of the animals and seed plants. The seeds and plants prayed for, fell into the basket and the animals gathered outside of her hogan.

At this time White Bead Woman received another name, Receive-Things-in-her-Hand . . ., because of this. Some of the animals she put into her basket and some who were left over had to walk. The cattle had been made out of Mirage Quartz Rock by White Bead Woman. She took Mirage Quartz Rock powder and water and molded them into the right shape and size. When she placed them in water they became alive.

They were told, "You will be dangerous and even your voices will be danger, but you will be used for good. You are to be used by the Earth People." She had it in her mind to do things this way. The Supreme Sacred Wind did not tell her to do this. These cattle were placed in baskets of white shell. When White Bead Woman traveled west, she took out a male and female cattle and put them in the spring at Fierce Water Spring at Pasture Canyon. No others, not her sons or the Sun or Frog Man had any cattle. These cattle were for all the Earth People.

Besides the animals in the basket she placed inside seeds, nuts, berries and roots. Her basket was made out of shell and had a finish on top of it, just like the marriage basket. These baskets of all five colors are still in the ocean where they were left by White Bead Woman. Some of the animals were left over and could not be carried in the basket, so they followed her to the west. . . . When she started from her New Mexican home, White Bead Woman spent a night at Red Mesa, near where Tuba City, Arizona, is now.

While she was spending the night there with her animals, they moved around in a circle and would not settle down. White Bead Woman made three posts out of black rock. These are the rocks that are found near where Tuba City is, now called Black Butte, another near Navaho Mountain called Wildcat Butte and one in Colorado called Black Post Butte. . . . The animals were thus enclosed by these mountains and the Little and Big Colorado Rivers.

After the animals became calm during the night, she went to the canyon where the water meets from the two great rivers. . . .

White Bead Woman sat there by the bank and then stepped back from the water. She then made a fire and prepared to stay the night. There is a gap down in the canyon where this happened. As she sat there, there appeared a fine young man out of the water called Sea Horse. This man looked like a horse, yet was a man. She spent a night with this man upon ground which was solid or hard. The next morning White Bead Woman had blood coming from her vagina, and this was the first period or menstruation in the world. The animals outside of her basket were later lost because of this infidelity. She left there as a gift to this man, salt, shell, turquoise, jet, white bead, oyster shell and red shell. These things are still there to this day. These gifts were all for this man.

After she had done this, she urinated into the Little Colorado and that is why it is now red as it runs into the Big Colorado. The next morning she went back to the top of the mountain where she had left all of her animals. As she got to the top of the mountain, she found all of her animals gone. On the west of Cedar Ridge is a mountain that was originally the escaped wild sheep from the herds of White Bead Woman. All of the wild sheep and most of the animals who escaped later turned into mountains. All of these animals that did not turn into mountains went into the Kaibab Forest and are still there. That is the reason there are so many game animals there now.

Near the joining of the two rivers is another gap where White Bead Woman went across with the few animals left in the basket. (There were still left the deer, antelope, all of the meat animals, turquoise, berries, corn, squash, etc.) She ate some of the corn seeds for her lunch on the way to the west. She went on to Mesa Verde and to ch·ōsgí. There is a pattern of the Sun there—a sand painting. It is still there and people pray to this Sun and no one can go there unless he has the right prayer.

It is important because White Bead Woman made the Sun pattern. It was made on a rock, and planted near there was a plant called Black Medicine . . . and a plant called Big or Large Medicine . . . . These two medicines are used in many ways and for many things. She brought the plants with her from the east. If anything goes wrong on the earth, the pattern looks old, and if everything is well, the pattern looks new. The location of the pattern is not known. She planted oak trees further on. Near these she piled some rocks for a marker to tell the trail which she called Pile-of-Rocks.

White Bead Woman continued on to Hopi Towers and on to Gray Mountain and on to the south side of Grand Canyon. She went right on until she arrived at the sea near the highest mountain in California, Mount Whitney. All of the people gathered around her when she arrived. All of the gods living near this area gathered and some even came from the home of White Bead Woman to the east. On top of this mountain was a hogan. If you look there now, it is still there. If you should look at this hogan when things are going bad, then it will look old. If it looks new, then affairs in the world are going to be good.

There are many things on the top of this mountain such as turquoise, flints, black shining dirt, pollen, white bead, horses of stone and many other things. All things that the medicine men made use of then and now can be found there. One of the gods picked up a boy and girl when they came from the east. He took them so that these children could be taught all the songs of the gods before they [the gods] left the earth. White Bead Woman knew all of the songs which the rest of the gods did not. These children were to learn everything from her.

The gods did not have soap-weed in the west where they were, so they had a talk to decide what to use for soap in the ceremonies. . . . The gods finally decided to bury jet, flint, white bead, oyster shell and turquoise so that a plant of soap would grow. They planted these things in the evening and the sing was held over the boy and girl all during the night.

The sing was held because these children had learned all from the White Bead Woman. They now could instruct the rest of the people while White Bead Woman was gone to the west. The dance was held now and the gods danced over the side of these seed materials. These seeds soon began to grow. In the morning they dug up the yucca and were now ready to make soap. During the ceremony they put plants underneath a basket which were pinyon, cedar, evergreen, fir, spruce and kinds of plants, but no pine. The basket was made of white bead like before and was about the size of a marriage basket.

At the time of the sing over the children, the War Twins did not know that it was taking place, but they heard a rumor about it. The First Twin started off with a friend, God-Water-Carrier. The First Twin had gone to this friend and told him to go on a journey with him. . . .

Inside the hogan, the First Twin asked his mother. "Why didn't you tell me you were here and that this ceremony was going on? Am I the wrong kind of a god? Why didn't you notify me? Aren't I entitled to be notified?" White Bead Woman answered her son saying, "I know you have nothing to do or say about what is going on out here. That is why we did not notify you."

Then the Twin said. "Have these children learned all the power that they are going to learn?" These children were still Earth People and not yet gods. "Is there any more for them to learn?" White Bead Woman said, "No, this is why we have picked these children. The people did not learn all of my power. I am going away with all the power, but now all of your Earth People will know everything." The Twins were gods and there were also many gods all over the world. The War Gods and the other gods at times were bad, disobedient, and not right. That is why she was "so stingy" with her knowledge. No one knew as much as she did about the ways of the world.

After White Bead Woman had answered her son, he said, "It is fine that these children know all and have all the power." He asked another question, "Did they learn the Good Way Song? Did they learn all the songs of the Five Night Sings? Did they learn the War Songs? Did they learn the Yeibache Songs? Did they learn all the other songs?" She answered saying, "It is all complete. All of these things have been learned. Now I do not have to worry about anything." They had all the power gained from knowing these things for they were not gods, but humans. That night the people finished the singing. In the morning the gods decided to send the children back with the Navaho—after they were to create them.

White Bead Woman in the morning took dirt from her chest and made the figures of two people. From her back she took more dirt and molded two more figures. From her right palm she molded two more figures. From the left palm she took dirt and once again molded two small figures. From the right foot dirt was taken and from the left more dirt and molded into figures. At last there were twelve small figures of humans—half of the figures women and half men. . . .

The people who were created were Navaho. The dirt had been taken and molded into figures like us, but very tiny. All of them were laid on the ground with a Never-Been-Shot-Buckskin put over the top and with one on the bottom. These figures were prayed and sung over by the White Bead Woman, Talking God and all of the other gods. After this was done, these small figures came to life and grew to full size. These people were to be called Created-Navaho, diné 'alya·ígí. These twelve people were then sent along with the two children to the east where the gods had been in the beginning.

After all this had happened, White Bead Woman continued to the west. . . . White Bead Woman started off, and the gods went to places where they were to stay forever. Some of the gods went into the earth, some into the heavens, some into the mountains and some into the water. These gods became settled and said, "From now on no person shall see us again."

. . . .

White Bead Woman went out to the Sun's house that was in the sea. Some medicine men say she traveled on foot to the west, but she is a god and does not travel in this way. The house of the Sun was sitting on the ocean, but was not an island. Sometimes people see it, but not all of the time. It was made of turquoise, white bead, jet and oyster shell. White Bead Woman looked at the house and blew a rainbow spectrum to the house. She got on it and rode to the house on the ocean. . . . White Bead Woman reached the Sun's house in the evening.

The Sun was glad to see her and he laughed and kissed her because of his happiness. Everything was in the house that she needed. The house was made as follows: The floor of the middle room was made of oyster shell polished like marble. The walls were also of oyster shell. To the east room the floor and walls were of polished white bead. To the south were floors and walls of turquoise. To the west there was again a room of oyster shell. In the last room, to the north, were black jet walls and floor. This house was like the Sun's house to the east.

This house also had clouds on all of the walls. In the middle room was a white male and female cloud on the wall. To the south was a blue male and female cloud. To the west was a yellow male and female cloud. Upon the north wall was a black male and female cloud. In this house were also seen the mortar and pestle in the floor and the many flints on the walls. After White Bead Woman had been there four days, she began getting old age (about 400 years old). If White Bead Woman had not gotten old at this time, it would not have been possible for old age to come about now.

After these four days had passed, she went into the east room, and when she came out, she was younger. After going into each of the rooms and finally coming out of the last one to the north, she was again a young girl. Even today she gets very old every four years, and she has to go through this procedure. Because of the four rooms, she will get young every four years, too. First Man and First Woman live at the east in the Sun's house, and they, too, get old every four years. They, too must do the same as the White Bead Woman.

All the other gods became old every twelve years, and when this happens, they all come together. There is a meeting place which is at another Black Mountain on the other side of Holbrook called Woodruff Buttes . . . . These gods have a meeting there every night to talk matters over. Anyone who wants to can hear these gods. These gods, unlike the others talked about, become young every twelve years. They, too, have a house so that when they get old, they can go through it and become young again.

The Sun also gets old like the other gods and has to go through his house so that he will get young again. White Bead Woman spent most of her time in the middle or center room. It was at this time that she got the name of Changing Woman, or Woman-Who-Changes. The house to the east is made the same as the one to the west. The Sun's other wife lives there.

You must teach your children that the ground beneath their feet is the ashes of your grandfathers. So that they will respect the land, tell your children that the earth is rich with the lives of our kin. Teach your children what we have taught our children, that the earth is our mother. Whatever befalls the earth befalls the sons of the earth. If men spit upon the ground, they spit upon themselves.
*~ **Unknown** ~*

The Origin of Corn
(Natchez)
[Corn Goddess Tale I]
from John R. Swanton, *Myths and Tales of the Southeastern Indians* (1929)

Corn-woman lived at a certain place in company with twin girls. When the corn was all gone, she went into the corn house, taking two baskets, and came out with the baskets full. They lived on the hominy which she made from this.

One time the girls looked into this corn house and saw nothing there. They said to each other, "Where does she get it? Next time she goes in there we will creep up and watch her."

When the corn was all gone, she started to go in and they saw her. So they crept after her and when she entered and closed the door, they peeped through a crack. They saw her set down the basket, stand astride of it and rub and shake herself, and there was a noise, tsågak, as if something fell off. In this way she filled one basket with corn. Then she stood over the other, rubbed herself and shook, the noise tsågak was heard and that basket was full of beans. After that the girls ran away.

"Let us not eat it," they said. "She defecates and then feeds us with the excrement." So when the hominy was cooked they did not eat it, and from that she knew they had seen her. "Since you think it is filthy, you will have to help yourselves from now on. Kill me and burn my body. When summer comes things will spring up on the place where it was burned and you must cultivate them, and when they are matured they will be your food."

They killed Corn-woman and burned her body and when summer came corn, beans, and pumpkins sprang up. They kept cultivating these and every day, when they stopped, stuck their hoes up in the ground and went away. But on their return more ground would be hoed and the hoes would be sticking up in different places.

They said, "Let us creep up and find out who is hoeing for us," and they did so. When they looked they saw that the hoes were doing it of themselves and they laughed. Immediately the hoes fell down and did not work for them anymore. They did not know that it was just those two hoes which were helping them and they themselves spoiled it.

Origin of
Corn *(Ababnaki)*

[Corn Goddess Tale
II]
from Stith Thompson,
*Tales of the North
American Indians* (1929)

A long time ago,
when Indians were
first made, there lived
one alone, far, far
from any others. He
knew not of fire, and
subsisted on roots,
barks, and nuts. This
Indian became very
lonesome for
company. He grew
tired of digging roots,
lost his appetite, and for several days lay dreaming in the sunshine;
when he awoke he saw something standing near, at which, at first,
he was very much frightened. But when it spoke, his heart was
glad, for it was a beautiful woman with long *light* hair, very unlike
any Indian. He asked her to come to him, but she would not, and if
he tried to approach her she seemed to go farther away; he sang to
her of his loneliness and besought her not to leave him; at last she
told him, if he would do just as she should say, he would always
have her with him. He promised that he would.

She led him to where there was some very dry grass, told him to
get two very dry sticks, rub them together quickly, holding them in
the grass. Soon a spark flew out; the grass caught it, and quick as
an arrow the ground was burned over. Then she said, "When the
sun sets, take me by the hair and drag me over the burned ground."

He did not like to do this, but she told him that wherever he dragged her something like grass would spring up, and he would see her hair coming from between the leaves; then the seeds would be ready for his use. He did as she said, and to this day, when they see the silk (hair) on the cornstalk, the Indians know she has not forgotten them.

The Hunter and
Selu *(Cherokee)*
[Corn Goddess Tale III]
from James Mooney, *Nineteenth Annual Report of the Bureau of American Ethnology 1897-98*, Part I. (1900)

A hunter had been tramping over the mountains all day long without finding any game and when the sun went down, he built a fire in a hollow stump, swallowed a few mouthfuls of corn gruel and lay down to sleep, tired out and completely discouraged. About the middle of the night he dreamed and seemed to hear the sound of beautiful singing, which continued until near daybreak and then appeared to die away into the upper air.

All next day he hunted with the same poor success, and at night made his lonely camp again, in the woods. He slept and the strange dream came to him again, but so vividly that it seemed to him like an actual happening. Rousing himself before daylight, he still heard the song, and feeling sure now that it was real, he went in the direction of the sound and found that it came from a single green stalk of corn (*selu*). The plant spoke to him, and told him to cut off some of its roots and take them to his home in the settlement, and the next morning to chew them and "go to water" before anyone else was awake, and then to go out again into the woods, and he would kill many deer and from that time on would always be successful in the hunt. The corn plant continued to talk, teaching him hunting secrets and telling him always to be generous with the game he took, until it was noon and the sun was high, when it suddenly took the form of a woman and rose gracefully into the air and was gone from sight, leaving the hunter alone in the woods.

He returned home and told his story, and all the people knew that he had seen Selu, the wife of Kana'tï. He did as the spirit had directed, and from that time was noted as the most successful of all the hunters in the settlement.

In the beginning of all things,
wisdom and knowledge were with the animals,
for Tirawa, the One Above, did not speak
directly to man. He sent certain animals
to tell men that he showed himself
through the beast, and that from them,
and from the stars and the sun and moon
should man learn.. all things tell of
Tirawa. All things in the world are two.
In our minds we are two, good and evil.
With our eyes we see two things, things
that are fair and things that are ugly....
We have the right hand that strikes and
makes for evil, and we have the left
hand full of kindness, near the heart.
One foot may lead us to an evil way,
the other foot may lead us to a good.
So are all things two, all two.

Eagle Chief (Letakos-Lesa) Pawnee

Paíyatuma and the Maidens of the Corn *(Zuñi)*

from Padraic Colum, *Orpheus: Myths of the World* (1930, copyright not renewed)

Whence came they, the Maidens who are told of in the stories and sung of in the songs of our Fathers, the seven Maidens with their magic wands and plumes who were lovelier than the seven bright stars that are above us now? Paíyatuma the Flute-player, the God of Dew and of the Dawn, brought them to our Fathers; they were his foster-children. And when he had brought them to where our Fathers were, he sang a song that warned all who were there that these were virgins and must be forever held as sacred beings. Paíyatuma sang:

> The corn that ye see growing upward
> Is the gift of my seven bright maidens:
> Look well that ye nourish their persons,
> Nor change ye the gift of their being
> As fertile of flesh for all men
> To the bearing of children for men,
> Lest ye lose them, and seek them in vain.

The mists of the morning were clearing away. Even as his voice had already gone into them, Paíyatuma the Flute-playing God went into the mists. Seven plants of corn he had left before our Fathers; seven Maidens he had left who would cause the corn to grow. "Thanks, thanks to thee, O Paíyatuma," our Fathers cried into the mists that closed round him. "Verily we will cherish the Maidens and the substance of their flesh."

Thereafter, as the season came round, our Fathers would build for the Maidens a bower of cedar-wood that was roofed with timbers brought from beyond the mountains. They would light a fire before the bower. All night, backwards and forwards, the Corn Maidens would dance to the music of drum and rattle and the songs sung by the elders. They would dance by the side of the seven growing plants of the corn, motioning them upward with their magic wands and plumes.

Then the first Maiden would embrace the first growing plant. As she did this the fire would leap up, throwing out a yellow light. The second Maiden would embrace the second growing plant, and the fire would burn smokily with a fuller grasping of the brands; blue would be the light the fire would throw out. The third Maiden would embrace the third of the growing plants, and at this the fire would reach to the fullness of its mastery, and the light it would throw out would be red. Then the fourth Maiden would embrace the fourth growing plant, and the fire, flameless now, would throw out a white light. As the fifth Maiden embraced the fifth growing plant the fire would give up its breath in clouds of sparks and its light would be streaked with many colours. The sixth Maiden would embrace the sixth growing plant; the fire would be sleeping then, giving out less light than heat. And as the seventh Maiden embraced the seventh growing plant the fire would waken afresh in the wind of the morning, and, as the fire of the wanderer stays glowing with many colours, it would stay glowing. Beautiful the dance of the seven Maidens, delightful the music they would dance to. And when the mists of the morning came they would go within the bower and lay down their magic wands and plumes, and their soft and shining dresses, and thereafter they would mingle with the people.

All rejoiced in the dance of the white-robed Corn Maidens. But a time came when certain of the young men of the village began to speak of a music they heard sounding from Thunder Mountain. This music was more wonderful than the music we had for the dance of the Maidens. And the young men declared that the dance that went to it, the dance they had not seen, must be more wonderful than the dance that our Maidens were praised for. They spoke of these things so often that they made our dance seem a thing that was of little worth. Then the Fathers summoned two messengers and bade them take the trail that went up the mountain. They were to find out about the music and the dance. Perchance they might be joined with ours, and a music and a dance that would seem wonderful to all might be given between the bower and the fire.

The messengers took the trail that went up Thunder Mountain. As they climbed they heard the sound of flutes. They went within the cavern that the music was being played in--the Cavern of the Rainbow. Mists surrounded them as they went within; but they knew what being was there, and they made reverence to him. Here was Paíyatuma the Flute-player, the God of Dew and of the Dawn.

They heard the music and they saw the dance that was being given in the Cavern of the Rainbow. The music was not as our music, for the musicians were flute-players. The Maidens who danced were as beautiful as our Corn Maidens; seven were they also. They carried in their hands wands of cottonwood: from the branchlets and buds of these wands streamlets flowed. "They are like your Maidens as the House of the Seven Stars seen in water is like the House of the Seven Stars as it is in the sky. They are fertile, not of seed, but of the Water of Life wherein the seed is quickened." So said Paíyatuma, the God of Dew and of the Dawn. And when the messengers looked upon them they saw that the Maidens were taller than ours were, and that their color was fainter.

Then did Paíyatuma lift up his flute and play upon it. A drum sounded also, and the cavern shook as with thunder. And as the music was played a white mist came from the flutes of the players. "Athirst are men ever for that which they have not," said Paíyatuma the Flute-player through the mist. "It is well that ye have come, and it shall be as ye wish," said he to the messengers. They knew then that he was aware of what errand they had been sent upon.

They went back and told the elders of the village that Paíyatuma's flute-players would come amongst them and make music for the dance of the Corn Maidens. The flute-players came down to the dancing-ground. Out of their bower came our white-clad, beautiful Corn Maidens. The flute-players lifted up their flutes and made music for the dance. And as the Maidens danced in the light of the fire, they who played the flutes looked on them in such wise that they [the maidens] were fain to let their hair fall down and cast down their eyes. Seeing the players of the flutes look on the Maidens amorously, our own youths looked on them amorously also. They plucked at their garments as they, in their dancing, came near them. Then the players of the flutes and our own youths sprang up and followed them, shouting and laying unseemly hands upon the beautiful, white-clad maidens.

Yet they finished their dance, and the seventh Maiden embraced the seventh growing plant. The mists came down, and unseen, the Maidens went into their bower. They laid their magic wands and their plumes upon the ground; they laid their white robes down also. Then they stole away. They were gone when Paíyatuma appeared. He came forth from the mists and stood amongst the assembled people. The flute-players, waving their flutes over the people who were there, followed Paíyatuma as he strode, wordless, through the mists that were rolling up the mountain.

The drum was beaten, the rattles were shaken, but still the Maidens did not come forth from their bower. The Elders went within and they found naught there but the wands and plumes and the garments that had been laid away. Then it was known that the Corn Maidens had gone. Grief and dismay filled the hearts of the people. "We must seek for and find our Maidens," they all cried, "for lacking them the corn-seed, which is the life of the flesh, cannot flourish." But where could one go seeking? The Maidens had left no trail behind them. . . .

[The people ask for help from the Eagle, the Falcon, and the Raven, but the corn maidens cannot be found.]

Our Fathers . . . knew now that neither the Eagle, the Falcon, nor the Raven could find and bring back to them their Maidens white and beautiful, the Maidens who could make grow the plants without which life of flesh cannot flourish. Only Paíyatuma could find them and bring them back. They came upon him outside the village. . . .

And Paíyatuma was in his daylight mood. His dress was soiled and torn, his eyes were bleared, and with uncouth mouth he was muttering uncouth words. He laughed at and joked with our Fathers when they came up to where he lolled--like a clown he laughed at and jested with them. And when they begged him to come with them he rose up and went with them as to some boys' performance. He strode rudely into where the Council was being held, and he greeted all who were there noisily and without dignity or shame. And when our Fathers, lamenting, begged him to find for them and bring back to them the Corn Maidens whom he had once brought to them, he shouted, "Why find that which is not lost nor summon those who will not come?"

Like a clown Paíyatuma behaved at the Council, and like a clown he would have gone on behaving if a certain priest who was there had not gone to him, and put his hand between his lips, and stroked away what was on his lips. "Thou hast drawn from me the breath of reversal," said Paíyatuma. "Purify yourselves now and I shall speak to you as it is becoming in me to speak to you." No longer was he a clown, talking thoughtlessly, speaking words that shamed his own sacred being. No, Paíyatuma stood before the Fathers, tall and grand as a great tree that has been shorn by lightning. Verily, again they knew him for the God of Dew and of the Dawn.

In his presence they purified themselves, putting away from them all that disgraced them in his eyes. From the youths in the village they chose four who had not sinned in their flesh. These four youths they brought to Paíyatuma.

And with the four youths he set out for Summerland. Where he paused he played upon his flute, and butterflies and birds came around him and fed upon the dew that was breathed forth from his flute. In a little while he came to Summerland. The seven Maidens of the Corn were there. They heard his flute-playing, and when they saw his tall form coming through the fields of corn that was already quickened they went to meet him. The butterflies and the birds came and fluttered over them--over the seven Maidens of the Corn, over the four youths from the village, over Paíyatuma, as he played upon his flute.

Back to the village they went, the Maidens, the four youths, and Paíyatuma. O greatly did the people rejoice at having their Maidens back once more amongst them. The bower was built and the fire was lighted as before. All night, backwards and forwards, the Corn Maidens danced to music and to songs sung by the elders. They danced by the side of the seven growing plants, motioning them upwards. And as each Maiden embraced the plant that was hers, the fire threw out its yellow light, its blue light, its red light, its white light, its streaked light, its dim light, its light of many colours.

Ah, but as each Maiden embraced her growing plant, she put into the corn and, by a mystery, the substance of her flesh. Then, as that light of many colours was thrown from the fire, the Maidens went forth as shadows. Into the deep night they went, and they were seen no more of men. The dawn came and the Fathers saw Paíyatuma standing with folded arms before the fire. Solemnly he spoke to them all; well have the solemn words he uttered then been remembered. The corn would grow because of the substance of their flesh that the Corn Maidens had put in it; in future seasons maidens chosen from amongst our own daughters would dance backwards and forwards to the music of the flute as well as the drum, and would embrace the seven growing plants in the light of the fire. And all would be well for the growth of the corn. But as for the Maidens white and beautiful whom he had twice brought to us, they were gone from us forever. "They have departed since the children of men would seek to change the sustaining blessedness of their flesh into humanity which sustains not, but is sustained. In the loving of men and the cherishing of men's children, they--even they--would forget the cherishing of their beautiful seed-growing. The Mother-maidens have gone, but their substance is in the plants of corn."

For that reason the corn that is for seed is held by us as a thing sacred. Through the nights and days of the Moon Nameless, of the Moon of Sacred Fire and Earth, of the Moon of Earth Whitening, of the Moon of Snow-broken Boughs, of the Moon of Snowless Pathways, of the Moon of Lesser Sand-driving Storms, the seed of the corn is held. Then it is put in the earth reverently; it is buried as a tribe might bury its beloved dead. The seed which has in it the substance of our Maiden-mothers becomes quick beneath the earth. Paíyatuma, the God of Dew and of the Dawn, freshens the growth with his breath; then Ténatsali, the God of Time and of the Seasons, brings the plants to maturity; then Kwélele, the God of Heat, ripens them with the touch of his Fire-brother's torch, giving them their full vitality. And our own maidens dance beside the corn-plants in the light of the fire, motioning them upwards-- upwards.

All things share the same breath - the beast, the tree, the man, the air shares its spirit with all the life it supports. *Chief Seattle*

Myth of the White Buffalo Woman *(Sioux)*

from Edward S. Curtis, *The North American Indian,* Vol. 3 (1908), pp. 56-60

Many generations ago, when the Lakota still dwelt beside the lake far away in the east, they experienced a winter of terrible severity. The snow lay deep on the ground, and the streams were frozen to their very beds. Every day could be heard the sharp crack of trees as the frost gnawed at their hearts; and at night the piles of skins and the blazing fires in the teepees scarcely sufficed to keep the blood coursing through the veins. Game seemed to have deserted the country, for though the hunters often faced the hardships of the winter chase, they returned empty-handed, and the wail of hungry women and children joined with the moan of the forest. When finally a tardy spring arrived, it was decided to leave a country so exposed to the anger of Wazíya, Spirit of the North, and seek a better homeland in the direction of the sunset, where ruled the Wing Flappers, who existed from the beginning.

There was little enough to pack besides teepees and fur robes, and what few dogs had not been eaten were soon harnessed to the laden travois. Two young men were sent in advance. No pair could have been more different in their nature than these two, for while one was brave, chivalrous, unselfish, and kind, the other's heart was bad, and he thought only of the sensuous and vicious.

Unencumbered as they were, the scouts were soon far ahead of the wearily dragging line of haggard men, women bent under burdens that dogs should have been drawing, straggling children, and a few gaunt dogs tugging at the over laden travois. Late in the day the scouts succeeded in shooting a deer, and thinking their people would reach that point for the night's camp, they left it where it had fallen and were turning away to seek other game when one of them felt a sudden impulse to look back. Wonderful sight! There in a mist that rose above a little hill appeared the outline of a woman. As they gazed in astonishment, the cloud slowly lifted, and the young men saw that she was a maiden fair and beautiful. Her only dress was a short skirt, wristlets, and anklets, all of sage. In the crook of her left arm she carried a bundle wrapped closely in a red buffalo-skin; on her back was a quiver, and in her left hand she held a bunch of herbs. Straightway the young man whose heart was evil was overpowered by a desire to possess the beautiful woman, but his companion endeavored to dissuade him with the caution that she might be . . . a messenger from the Great Mystery.

"No, no!" he cried vehemently, "she is not holy, but a woman, human like ourselves, and I will have her!"

Without waiting he ran toward the woman, who forthwith warned him that she was a sacred being. When he persisted and went closer, she commanded him sternly to stop, for his heart was evil and he was unworthy to come near to the holy things she bore. As he still advanced, she retreated, laid her burden on the ground, and then came toward him. Suddenly it appeared to the waiting youth that the mist descended and enveloped the mysterious woman and his companion. Then followed a fearful sound of rattling and hissing as of thousands of angered rattlesnakes. The terrified observer was about to flee from the dreadful place when the cloud lifted as suddenly as it had descended, disclosing the bleached bones of his former comrade, and the beautiful virgin standing calmly beside them. She spoke to him gently, bidding him have no fear, for he was chosen to be priest of his nation.

"I have many things to impart to your people," she said. "Go now to the place where they are encamped, and bid them prepare for my coming. Build a great circle of green boughs, leaving an opening at the east. In the centre erect a council teepee, and over the ground inside spread sage thickly. In the morning I shall come."

Filled with awe, the young man hastened back and delivered to his people the message of the holy woman. Under his direction her commands were reverently obeyed, for were they not a message from the Great Mystery? In the morning, gathered within the circle of green boughs, they waited in great expectancy, looking for the messenger of the Mystery to enter through the opening left at the east. Suddenly, obeying a common impulse, they turned and looked in the opposite direction, and behold! she stood before them.

Entering the teepee with a number of just and upright men selected by the youth whom she had chosen to receive the sacred rites, she at once spread open the red buffalo-skin, exposing its contents-- tobacco, the feather of a spotted eagle, the skin of a red-headed woodpecker, a roll of buffalo-hair, a few braids of sweet-grass, and, chief of all, a red stone pipe with the carved image of a buffalo calf surmounting its wooden stem. At the same time she explained that the Great Mystery had sent her to reveal to them his laws, and teach them how to worship, that they might become a great and powerful people.

During the four days she remained with them in the teepee she instructed them in the customs they were to observe--how the man who would have great [spiritual] power should go into the high places and fast for many days, when he would see visions and obtain strength from the Mysteries; how to punish him of evil heart who sinned against the rights of his brother; how to instruct girls at maturity, and to care for the sick. She taught them also how to worship the Great Mystery. . . .

Then she taught them carefully the five great ceremonies they were to observe: . . . the Foster-parent Chant, the Sun Dance, the Vision Cry, the Buffalo Chant, and the Ghost Keeper. The sacred pipe she gave into the keeping of the chosen young man, with the admonition that its wrapping should be removed only in cases of direst tribal necessity. From the quiver on her back she took six bows and six arrows, and distributed them among as many young men, renowned for their bravery, hospitality, and truthfulness. These weapons she bade them take, after her departure, to the summit of a certain hill, where they would find a herd of six hundred buffalo, all of which they were to kill. In the midst of the herd would be found six men. These also they were to kill, then cut off their ears and attach them to the stem of the sacred pipe. Her last words were these:

"So long as you believe in this pipe and worship the Mystery as I have taught you, so long will you prosper; you will have food in plenty; you will increase and be powerful as a nation. But when you, as a people, cease to reverence the pipe, then will you cease to be a nation."

With these words she left the teepee and went to the opening at the eastern side of the camp-circle. Suddenly she disappeared, and the people, crowding forward to see what had become of her, beheld only a white buffalo cow trotting over the prairie.

The Great Spirit Names the Animal People: How Coyote Came by His Powers

(Okanogan)
from Mourning Dove
(Hum-isha-ma;
Christal Quintasket),
Coyote Tales (1933).

The Great Spirit called all his people together from all over the earth. There was to be a change. He would give names to the people, and the Animal World was to rule. The naming was to begin at the break of day, each one having the right to choose his or her name according to who came first to the Spirit Chief's lodge. The Spirit Chief would also give each one their duty to perform in the changed conditions.

It was the night before the New World. Excitement was among the people. Each one desired a great name of note. All wished to be awake and first at the lodge of the Great Spirit Chief. Everyone wanted power to rule some tribe, some kingdom of the Animal World.

Coyote was of a degraded nature, a vulgar type of life. He was an imitator of everything that he saw or heard. When he asked a question, when he asked for information and it was given him, he would always say, "I knew that before! I did not have to be told."

That was Coyote's way. He was hated by all the people for his ways. No one liked him. He boasted too much about his wisdom, about everything. Coyote went among the anxious people, bragging to everyone how early he was going to rise, how he would be the first one at the Spirit Chief's lodge. He bragged of the great name he would choose. He said, "I will have three big names to select from: there is Grizzly Bear, who will be ruler over all running, four-footed animals; Eagle, who will lead all the flying birds; Salmon, who will be chief over all the fish of every kind."

Coyote's twin brother, who took the name of Fox, said to him, "Do not be too sure. Maybe no one will be given his choice of names. Maybe you will have to retain your own name, Coyote. Because it is a degraded name, no one among the tribes will want to take it.

. . . .

Coyote went to his tepee in anger. He determined not to sleep that night. He would remain awake so as to be the first at the Spirit Chief's lodge for the name he wanted. . . . Coyote's wife (afterwards Mole), sat on her feet at the side of the doorway. She looked up at Coyote and said in a disappointed tone, "Have you no food for the children? They are starving! I can find no roots to dig."

"Eh-ha!" grunted Coyote sarcastically. He answered his wife, "I am no common person to be spoken to in that fashion by a mere woman. Do you know that I am going to be a great Chief at daybreak tomorrow? I shall be Grizzly Bear. I will devour my enemies with ease. I will take other men's wives. I will need you no longer. You are growing too old, too ugly to be the wife of a great warrior, of a big Chief as I will be."

. . . .

Coyote ordered his wife to gather plenty of wood for the tepee fire where he would sit without sleep all night. Half of the night passed; Coyote grew sleepy. His eyes would close however hard he tried to keep them open. Then he thought what to do. He took two small sticks and braced his eyelids apart. He must not sleep! But before Coyote knew it, he was fast asleep. He was awakened by his wife, Mole, when she returned from the Spirit Chief's lodge, when the sun was high in the morning sky. . . .

Coyote jumped up from where he lay. He hurried to the lodge of the Chief Spirit. Nobody was there, and Coyote thought that he was first. . . . He went into the lodge and spoke, "I am going to be Grizzly Bear!"

The Chief answered, "Grizzly Bear was taken at daybreak!"

Coyote said, "Then I shall be called Eagle!"

The Chief answered Coyote, "Eagle has chosen his name. He flew away long ago."

Coyote then said, "I think that I will be called Salmon."

The Spirit Chief informed Coyote, "Salmon has also been taken. All the names have been used except your own: Coyote. No one wished to steal your name from you."

Poor Coyote's knees grew weak. He sank down by the fire in that great tepee. The heart of the Spirit Chief was touched when he saw the lowered head of Coyote, the mischief-maker. After a silence the Chief spoke, "You are Coyote! You are the hated among all the tribes, among all the people. I have chosen you from among all others to make you sleep, to go to the land of the dream visions. I make a purpose for you, a big work for you to do before another change comes to the people. You are to be father for all the tribes, for all the new kind of people who are to come. Because you are so hated, degraded and despised, you will be known as the Trick-person. You will have power to change yourself into anything, any object you wish when in danger or distress. There are man-eating monsters on the earth who are destroying the people. The tribes cannot increase and grow as I wish. These monsters must all be vanquished before the new people come. This is your work to do. I give you powers to kill these monsters. I have given your twin brother, Fox, power to help you, to restore you to life should you be killed. Your bones may be scattered; but if there is one hair left on your body, Fox can bring you back to life. Now go, despised Coyote! Begin the work laid out for your trail. Do good for the benefit of your people."

Thus, Coyote of the Animal People was sent about the earth to fight and destroy the people-devouring monsters, to prepare the land for the coming of the new people, the Indians. Coyote' eyes grew slant from the effects of the sticks with which he braced them open that night when waiting for the dawn of the name giving day. From this, the Indians have inherited their slightly slant eyes as descendants from Coyote.

Cherokee

May the warm winds of heaven blow softly on this house and the Great Spirit bless all who enter here.
Oh Great spirit, grant that I may never find fault with my neighbor until I have walked the trail of life in his moccasins.

Unknown

Manabozho and the "Hell-Diver"
(Menomini)
[The Duped Dancers]
from Stith Thompson, *Tales of the North American Indians* (1929)

While Manabozho was once walking along a lake shore, tired and hungry, he observed a long, narrow sandbar, which extended far out into the water, around which were myriads of waterfowl, so Manabozho decided to have a feast. He had with him only his medicine bag; so he entered the brush and hung it upon a tree, now called "Manabozho tree," and procured a quantity of bark, which he rolled into a bundle and placing it upon his back, returned to the shore, where he pretended to pass slowly by in sight of the birds. Some of the Swans and Ducks, however, recognizing Manabozho and becoming frightened, moved away from the shore.

One of the Swans called out, "Ho! Manabozho, where are you going?" To this Manabozho replied, "I am going to have a song. As you may see, I have all my songs with me." Manabozho then called out to the birds, "Come to me, my brothers, and let us sing and dance." The birds assented and returned to the shore, then all retreated a short distance away from the lake to an open space where they might dance. Manabozho removed the bundle of bark from his back and placed it on the ground, got out his singing-sticks, and said to the birds, "Now, all of you dance around me as I drum; sing as loudly as you can, and keep your eyes closed. The first one to open his eyes will forever have them red and sore."

Manabozho began to beat time upon his bundle of bark, while the birds, with eyes closed, circled around him singing as loudly as they could. Keeping time with one hand, Manabozho suddenly grasped the neck of a Swan, which he broke; but before he had killed the bird it screamed out, whereupon Manabozho said, "That's right, brothers, sing as loudly as you can." Soon another Swan fell a victim; then a Goose, and so on until the number of birds was greatly reduced. Then the "Hell diver," opening his eyes to see why there was less singing than at first, and beholding Manabozho and the heap of victims, cried out, "Manabozho is killing us! Manabozho is killing us!" and immediately ran to the water, followed by the remainder of the birds.

As the "Hell-diver" was a poor runner, Manabozho soon overtook him, and said, "I won't kill you, but you shall always have red eyes and be the laughing-stock of all the birds." With this he gave the bird a kick, sending him far out into the lake and knocking off his tail, so that the "Hell-diver" is red-eyed and tailless to this day.

"Treat the earth well: it was not given to you by your parents, it was loaned to you by your children. We do not inherit the Earth from our Ancestors, we borrow it from our Children."

Unknown

Wakdjunkaga, Trickster
(Winnebago)
(Source unknown)

As he continued his aimless wandering, unexpectedly, much to his surprise, he met a little fox. "Well, my younger brother, here you are! You are traveling, aren't you?" "Yes, yes, here I am!" answered the little fox. "The world is going to be a difficult place to live in and I am trying to find some clean place in which to dwell. That is what I am looking for." "Oh, oh, my younger brother, what you have said is very true. I, too, was thinking of the very same thing. I have always wanted to have a companion, so let us live together." Trickster consented, and so they went on to look for a place in which to dwell.

As they ran along they encountered a jay. "Well, well, my younger brother, what are you doing?" asked Trickster. "Older brother, I am looking for a place to live in because the world is soon going to be a difficult place in which to dwell."

"We are looking for the very same thing. When I heard my younger brother speaking of this I envied him very much. So let us live together, for we also are hunting for such a place." Thus spoke Trickster. Then they went on together and soon they came across a nit who also joined them. . . .

Winter soon approached and not long after it began, a deep snow fell. The situation of the four now became indeed very difficult. They had nothing to eat and they were getting quite hungry. . . . Then Trickster spoke: "Listen. There is a village yonder, where they are enjoying great blessings. The chief has a son who is killing many animals. He is not married yet but is thinking of it. Let us go over there. I will disguise myself as a woman and marry

him. Thus we can live in peace until spring comes." "Good!" they
ejaculated. All were willing and delighted to participate.

Trickster now took an elk's liver and made a vulva from it. Then he
took some elk's kidneys and made breasts from them. Finally he
put on a woman's dress. In this dress his friends enclosed him very
firmly. . . . He now stood there transformed into a very pretty
woman indeed. Then he let the fox have intercourse with him and
make him pregnant, then the jaybird and, finally, the nit. After that
he proceeded toward the village.

Now, at the edge of the village, lived an old woman and she
immediately addressed him, saying, "My granddaughter, what is
your purpose in traveling around like this? Certainly it is with
some object in view that you are traveling!" Then the old woman
went outside and shouted, "Ho! Ho! There is someone here who
has come to court the chief's son." This, at least, is what the old
woman seemed to be saying. Then the chief said to his daughters,
"Ho! This clearly is what this woman wants and is the reason for
her coming; so, my daughters, go and bring your sister-in-law
here." Then they went after her. She certainly was a very
handsome woman. The chief's son liked her very much.
Immediately they prepared dried corn for her and they boiled split
bear-ribs. That was why Trickster was getting married, of course.
When this food was ready they put it in a dish, cooled it, and
placed it in front of Trickster. He devoured it at once. There she
(Trickster) remained.

Not long after Trickster became pregnant. The chief's son was very
happy about the fact that he was to become a father. Not long after
that Trickster gave birth to a boy. Then again he became pregnant
and gave birth to another boy. Finally for the third time he became
pregnant and gave birth to a third boy. The last child cried as soon
as it was born and nothing could stop it. The crying became very
serious and so it was decided to send for an old woman who had
the reputation for being able to pacify children. She came, but she,

likewise, could not pacify him. Finally the little child cried out and sang: "If I only could play with a little piece of white cloud!"

They went in search of a shaman, for it was the chief's son who was asking for this and, consequently, no matter what the cost, it had to be obtained. . . . All tried very hard, and, finally, they made it snow. Then, when the snow was quite deep, they gave him a piece of snow to play with and he stopped crying.

After a while he again cried out and sang: "If I could only play with a piece of blue sky!"

Then they tried to obtain a piece of blue sky for him. Very hard they tried, but were not able to obtain any. In the spring of the year, however, they gave him a piece of blue grass and he stopped crying.

After a while he began to cry again. This time he asked for some blue (green) leaves. Then the fourth time he asked for some roasting ears. They gave him green leaves and roasting ears of corn and he stopped crying.

One day later, as they were steaming corn, the chief's wife teased her sister-in-law. She chased her around the pit where they were steaming corn. Finally, the chief's son's wife (Trickster) jumped over the pit and she dropped something very rotten. The people shouted at her, "It is Trickster!" The men were all ashamed, especially the chief's son. The animals who had been with Trickster, the fox, the jaybird and the nit, all of them now ran away.

The Origin of Eternal Death
(*Wishram*)

from Edward S. Curtis, *The North American Indian*, Vol. 8 (1911).

Coyote had a wife and two children, and so had Eagle. Both families lived together. Eagle's wife and children died, and a few days later Coyote experienced the same misfortune. As the latter wept, his companion said: "Do not mourn: that will not bring your wife back. Make ready your moccasins, and we will go somewhere." So the two prepared for a long journey, and set out westward.

After four days they were close to the ocean; on one side of a body of water they saw houses. Coyote called across, "Come with a boat!" "Never mind; stop calling," bade Eagle. He produced an elderberry stalk, made a flute, put the end into the water, and whistled. Soon they saw two persons come out of a house, walk to the water's edge, and enter a canoe. Said Eagle, "Do not look at those people when they land." The boat drew near, but a few yards from the shore it stopped, and Eagle told his friend to close his eyes. He then took Coyote by the arm and leaped to the boat. The two persons paddled back, and when they stopped a short distance from the other side Eagle again cautioned Coyote to close his eyes, and then leaped ashore with him.

They went to the village, where there were many houses, but no people were in sight. Everything was still as death. There was a very large underground house, into which they went. In it was found an old woman sitting with her face to the wall, and lying on the floor on the other side of the room was the moon. They sat down near the wall.

"Coyote," whispered Eagle, "watch that woman and see what she does when the sun goes down!" Just before the sun set they heard a voice outside calling: "Get up! Hurry! The sun is going down, and it will soon be night. Hurry, hurry!" Coyote and Eagle still sat in a corner of the chamber watching the old woman. People began to enter, many hundreds of them, men, women, and children. Coyote, as he watched, saw Eagle's wife and two daughters among them, and soon afterward his own family. When the room was filled, Nikshiamchasht, the old woman, cried, "Are all in?" Then she turned about, and from a squatting posture she jumped forward, then again and again, five times in all, until she alighted in a small pit beside the moon. This she raised and swallowed, and at once it was pitch dark. The people wandered about, hither and thither, crowding and jostling, unable to see. About daylight a voice from outside cried, "Nikshiamshasht, all get through!" The old woman then disgorged the moon, and laid it back in its place on the floor; all the people filed out, and the woman, Eagle, and Coyote were once more alone.

"Now, Coyote," said Eagle, "could you do that?" "Yes, I can do that," he said. They went out, and Coyote at Eagle's direction made a box of boards, as large as he could carry, and put into it leaves from every kind of tree and blades from every kind of grass. "Well," said Eagle, "If you are sure you remember just how she did this, let us go in and kill her." So they entered the house and killed her, and buried the body. Her dress they took off and put on Coyote, so that he looked just like her, and he sat down in her place. Eagle then told him to practice what he had seen, by turning around and jumping as the old woman had done. So Coyote tuned about and jumped five times, but the last leap was a little short, yet he managed to slide into the hole. He put the moon into his mouth, but, try as he would, a thin edge still showed, and he covered it with his hands. Then he laid it back in its place and resumed his seat by the wall, waiting for sunset and the voice of the chief outside.

The day passed, the voiced called, and the people entered. Coyote turned about and began to jump. Some thought there was something strange about the manner of jumping, but others said it was really the old woman. When he came to the last jump and slipped into the pit, many cried out that this was not the old woman, but Coyote quickly lifted the moon and put it into his mouth, covering the edge with his hands. When it was completely dark, Eagle placed the box in the doorway. Throughout the long night Coyote retained the moon in his mouth, until he was almost choking, but at last the voice of the chief was heard from the outside, and the dead began to file out. Every one walked into the box, and Eagle quickly threw the cover over and tied it. The sound was like that of a great swarm of flies. "Now, my brother, we are through," said Eagle. Coyote removed the dress and laid it down beside the moon, and Eagle threw the moon into the sky, where it remained. The two entered the canoe with the box, and paddled toward the east.

When they landed, Eagle carried the box. Near the end of the third night Coyote heard somebody talking; there seemed to be many voices. He awakened his companion, and said, "There are many people coming." "Do not worry," said Eagle; "it is all right." The following night Coyote heard the talking again, and, looking about, he discovered that the voices came from the box which Eagle had been carrying. He placed his ear against it, and after a while distinguished the voice of his wife. He smiled, and broke into laughter, but he said nothing to Eagle. At the end of the fifth night and the beginning of their last day of traveling, he said to his friend, "I will carry the box now; you have carried it a long way." "No," replied Eagle, "I will take it; I am strong." "Let me carry it," insisted the other; "suppose we come to where people live, and they should see the chief carrying the load. How would that look?" Still Eagle retained his hold on the box, but as they went along Coyote kept begging, and about noon, wearying of the subject, Eagle gave him the box. So Coyote had the load, and every time he heard the voice of his wife he would laugh. After a while he contrived to fall behind, and when Eagle was out of sight around a hill he began to open the box, in order to release his wife. But no sooner was the cover lifted than it was thrown back violently, and the dead people rushed out into the air with such force that Coyote was thrown to the ground. They quickly disappeared in the west. Eagle saw the cloud of dead people rising in the air, and came hurrying back. He found one man left there, a cripple who had been unable to rise; he threw him into the air, and the dead man floated away swiftly.

"You see what you have done, with your curiosity and haste!" said Eagle. "If we had brought these dead all the way back, people would not die forever, but only for a season, like these plants, whose leaves we have brought. Hereafter trees and grasses will die only in the winter, but in the spring they will be green again. So it would have been with the people." "Let us go back and catch them again," proposed Coyote; but Eagle objected: "They will not go to the same place, and we would not know how to find them; they will be where the moon is, up in the sky."

"LIKE A BROTHER"

I will draw thorns from your feet-
We will walk the white path of life together-
like a brother of my own blood-
I will love you-
I will wipe tears from your eyes-
I will put your aching heart to rest

Unknown

How Coyote Stole Fire
(Karok?)

Long ago, when man was newly come into the world, there were days when he was the happiest creature of all. Those were the days when spring brushed across the willow tails, or when his children ripened with the blueberries in the sun of summer, or when the goldenrod bloomed in the autumn haze.

But always the mists of autumn evenings grew more chill, and the sun's strokes grew shorter. Then man saw winter moving near, and he became fearful and unhappy. He was afraid for his children, and for the grandfathers and grandmothers who carried in their heads the sacred tales of the tribe. Many of these, young and old, would die in the long, ice-bitter months of winter.

Coyote, like the rest of the People, had no need for fire. So he seldom concerned himself with it, until one spring day when he was passing a human village. There the women were singing a song of mourning for the babies and the old ones who had died in the winter. Their voices moaned like the west wind through a buffalo skull, prickling the hairs on Coyote's neck.

"Feel how the sun is now warm on our backs," one of the men was saying. "Feel how it warms the earth and makes these stones hot to the touch. If only we could have had a small piece of the sun in our teepees during the winter."

Coyote, overhearing this, felt sorry for the men and women. He also felt that there was something he could do to help them. He knew of a faraway mountain-top where the three Fire Beings lived. These Beings kept fire to themselves, guarding it carefully for fear that man might somehow acquire it and become as strong as they. Coyote saw that he could do a good turn for man at the expense of these selfish Fire Beings.

So Coyote went to the mountain of the Fire Beings and crept to its top. He watched the way that the Beings guarded their fire. As he approached, the Beings leaped to their feet and gazed searchingly round their camp. Their eyes glinted like bloodstones, and their hands were clawed like the talons of the great black vulture.

"What's that? What's that I hear?" hissed one of the Beings.

"A thief, skulking in the bushes!" screeched another.

The third looked more closely, and saw Coyote.   But he had gone to the mountain-top on all fours, so the Being thought she saw only an ordinary coyote slinking among the trees.

"It is no one, it is nothing!" she cried, and the other two looked where she pointed and also saw only a grey coyote. They sat down again by their fire and paid Coyote no more attention.

So he watched all day and night as the Fire Beings guarded their fire. He saw how they fed it pine cones and dry branches from the sycamore trees. He saw how they stamped furiously on runaway rivulets of flame that sometimes nibbled outwards on edges of dry grass. He saw also how, at night, the Beings took turns to sit by the fire. Two would sleep while one was on guard; and at certain times the Being by the fire would get up and go into their teepee, and another would come out to sit by the fire.

Coyote saw that the Beings were always jealously watchful of their fire except during one part of the day. That was in the earliest morning, when the first winds of dawn arose on the mountains. Then the Being by the fire would hurry, shivering, into the teepee calling, "Sister, sister, go out and watch the fire." But the next

Being would always be slow to go out for her turn, her head spinning with sleep and the thin dreams of dawn.

Coyote, seeing all this, went down the mountain and spoke to his friends among the People. He told them of hairless man, fearing the cold and death of winter. And he told them of the Fire Beings, and the warmth and brightness of the flame. They all agreed that man should have fire, and they all promised to help Coyote's undertaking.

Then Coyote sped again to the mountain top. Again the Fire Beings leaped up when he came close, and one cried out, "What's that? A thief, a thief!"

But again the others looked closely, and saw only a grey coyote hunting among the bushes. So they sat down again and paid him no more attention.

Coyote waited through the day, and watched as night fell and two of the Beings went off to the teepee to sleep. He watched as they changed over at certain times all the night long, until at last the dawn winds rose.

Then the Being on guard called, "Sister, sister, get up and watch the fire."

And the Being whose turn it was climbed slow and sleepy from her bed, saying, "Yes, yes, I am coming. Do not shout so."

But before she could come out of the teepee, Coyote lunged from the bushes, snatched up a glowing portion of fire, and sprang away down the mountainside.

Screaming, the Fire Beings flew after him. Swift as Coyote ran, they caught up with him, and one of them reached out a clutching hand. Her fingers touched only the tip of the tail, but the touch was enough to turn the hairs white, and coyote tail tips are white still. Coyote shouted, and flung the fire away from him. But the others of the People had gathered at the mountain's foot. Squirrel saw the fire falling, and caught it, putting it on her back and fleeing away through the treetops. The fire scorched her back so painfully that her tail curled up and back, as squirrels' tails still do today.

The Fire Beings then pursued Squirrel, who threw the fire to Chipmunk. Chattering with fear, Chipmunk stood still as if rooted until the Beings were almost upon her. Then, as she turned to run, one Being clawed at her, tearing down the length of her back and leaving three stripes that are to be seen on chipmunks' backs even today. Chipmunk threw the fire to Frog, and the Beings turned towards him. One of the Beings grasped his tail, but Frog gave a mighty leap and tore himself free, leaving his tail behind in the Being's hand, which is why frogs have had no tails ever since.

As the Beings came after him again, Frog flung the fire on to Wood. And Wood swallowed it.

The Fire Beings gathered round, but they did not know how to get the fire out of Wood. They promised it gifts, sang to it and shouted at it. They twisted it and struck it and tore it with their knives. But Wood did not give up the fire. In the end, defeated, the Beings went back to their mountaintop and left the People alone.

But Coyote knew how to get fire out of Wood. And he went to the village of men and showed them how. He showed them the trick of rubbing two dry sticks together, and the trick of spinning a sharpened stick in a hole made in another piece of wood. So man was from then on warm and safe through the killing cold of winter.

The Lame Warrior
(An Arapaho Legend)

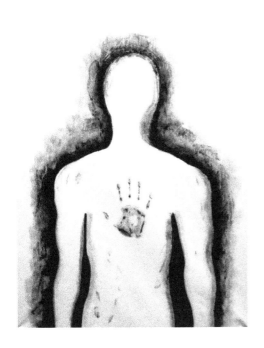

In the days before horses, a party of young Arapaho set off on foot one autumn morning in search of wild game in the western mountains. They carried heavy packs of food and spare moccasins, and one day as they were crossing the rocky bed of a shallow stream a young warrior felt a sudden sharp pain in his ankle. The ankle swelled and the pain grew worse until they pitched camp that night.

Next morning the warrior's ankle was swollen so badly that it was impossible for him to continue the journey with the others. His companions decided it was best to leave him. They cut young willows and tall grass to make a thatched shelter for him, and after the shelter was finished they collected a pile of dry wood so that he could keep a fire burning.

"When your ankle gets well," they told him, "don't try to follow us. Go back to our village, and await our return."

After several lonely days, the lame warrior tested his ankle, but it was still too painful to walk upon. And then one night a heavy snowstorm fell, virtually imprisoning him in the shelter. Because he had been unable to kill any wild game, his food supply was almost gone.

Late one afternoon he looked out and saw a large herd of buffalo rooting in the snow for grass quite close to his shelter. Reaching for his bow and arrow, he shot the fattest one and killed it. He then crawled out of the shelter to the buffalo, skinned it, and brought in the meat. After preparing a bed of coals, he placed a section of ribs in the fire for roasting.

Night had fallen by the time the ribs were cooked, and just as the lame warrior was reaching for a piece to eat, he heard footsteps crunching on the frozen snow. The steps came nearer and nearer to the closed flap of the shelter. "Who can that be?" he said to himself. "I am here alone and unable to run, but I shall defend myself if need be." He reached for his bow and arrow.

A moment later the flap opened and a skeleton clothed in a tanned robe stood there looking down at the lame warrior.

The robe was pinned tight at the neck so that only the skull was visible above and skeleton feet below. Frightened by this ghost, the warrior turned his eyes away from it.

"You must not be frightened of me," the skeleton said in a hoarse voice. "I have taken pity on you. Now you must take pity on me. Give me a piece of those roast ribs to eat, for I am very hungry."

Still very much alarmed by the presence of this unexpected visitor, the warrior offered a large piece of meat to an extended bony hand. He was astonished to see the skeleton chew the food with its bared teeth and swallow it.

"It was I who gave you the pain in your ankle," said the skeleton. "It was I who caused your ankle to swell so that you could not continue on the hunt. If you had gone on with your companions you would have been killed. The day they left you here, an enemy war party made a charge upon them, and they were all killed. I am the one who saved your life."

Again the skeleton's bony hand reached out, this time to rub the warrior's ankle. The pain and swelling vanished at once. "Now you can walk again," the ghost said. "Your enemies are all around, but if you will follow me I can lead you safely back to your village."

At dawn they left the shelter and started off across the snow, the skeleton leading the way. They walked through deep woods, along icy streams, and over high hills. Late in the afternoon the skeleton led the warrior up a steep ridge. When the warrior reached the summit, the ghost had vanished, but down in the valley below he could see the smokes of tepees in his Arapaho village.

"When you were born, you cried and the world rejoiced.
Live your life so that when you die, the world cries and you rejoice."

Cherokee Expression

The Stone Boy
(A Sioux Legend)

The Four Brothers lived together without any woman, so they did the woman's work. One time, as the eldest was gathering wood after nightfall, something ran into his big toe. This pained him but little and soon he forgot it, but his toe began to swell and was soon as big as his head. Then he cut it open and found something in it. He did not know what it was, but his brothers washed it and found that it was a baby girl.

The Four Brothers kept the baby and gave it good food and fine clothes so that it grew to be a beautiful young woman. She could do a woman's work well and quickly and never allowed anyone leave their teepee cold or hungry. She could dress skins so that they were white and soft and from them make good clothing, upon which she put beautiful ornaments, and each ornament meant something.

Many young men tried to induce her to live with them, but she would not leave the Four Brothers. They told her that they would always keep her as their sister, and they did everything to please her. The eldest brother said "I will go and hunt deer so that our sister may have the skins to make clothing for herself." He went away and did not return. Then the next eldest brother said, "I will go and hunt buffalo so that our sister may have the skins to make robes for herself." He went away and did not return. Then the next youngest brother said, "I will go and hunt Elk so that our sister may have meat for herself." He too went away and did not return. Then the youngest brother said, "Sister, our brothers have gone away and have not returned. I will go and find them." So he went away and did not return.

When the youngest brother had been gone one moon, the young woman went to the top of a high hill to mourn, and to seek a vision. While she was mourning she saw a pebble which she looked at for long time, for it was very smooth and white, and then she put it in her mouth to keep from being thirsty. She fell asleep with the pebble in her mouth and swallowed it. While she slept the vision came to her in the form of a great beast, which told her that the Four Brothers were kept by a stone and that a stone would find them and bring them back to her.

She told this vision to a Shaman and asked him to tell her what it meant. The Shaman told her to marry and name her son the Stone. But she would not live with any man, for she remembered how good and kind the Four Brothers were, and she wished to live with them only.

Soon she grew big with child and gave birth to a baby boy. The flesh of this baby was as hard as stone, and she knew that it was mysterious (Wakan) and came from the pebble she had swallowed. She went far away and lived alone with her son. She taught him all the games and songs and all about Roots and Plants and Animals and Birds, so that he was cunning and wise. She gave him fine clothes and good food so that he grew up strong and brave though his flesh and was hard as stone. She would not allow him to hunt or join a war party, for she was afraid he would go away and never return like the Four Brothers.

Each Moon she went to top of the hill to mourn. When her son had grown to be a man he asked to why she went to mourn each Moon, and she said to him, "My son, you are now a man, and I will tell you why I mourn." So she told him the story of the Four Brothers, of her coming to them, of how they went away and did not return, of his own birth and the vision of a great beast.

She sang this song to him:

I am a mysterious woman.
I am like no other woman.

You are a mysterious man.
Your flesh is like stone.

You are the Stone Boy.
You are the stone the great beast told of.

He then sang to her:

I am the Stone Boy.
I am the stone that will aid you.

I will bring back your brothers.
My mother, I will make you happy.

He then said to her, "Mother, I will go to find your brothers. I will
bring them to you." She said, "I am afraid you too will go away
and never come back." He said to her, "What did the great beast to
tell you? I am the stone." She said, "Go my son, but first you must
be prepared with magic." She made a great feast and invited a wise
Shaman, a wise old woman, a great brave, a great hunter and four
maidens as the chief guests, and all the people as common guests.
She placed the people as they belonged according to the bands,
with her son among the chief guests. When all were satisfied with
eating, she stood before the people and told the story of the Four
Brothers; of her coming to them, of their going, of her vision, and
birth and life of her son. She then told them to examine her son
that they might know that he was mysterious (Wakan). The people
all examined the young man, and when they found that his flesh
was hard like stone, they said he was indeed mysterious and that he
was the Stone Boy. She then told them that her son was to go in
quest of the Four Brothers and she had invited the chief guests so

that they would help her to prepare her son with the magic for his quest.

The chief guests agreed to do what she should ask of them. The Shaman gave the Stone Boy a charm (Pajuta-wakan-rea) that would keep all harm from him. The old woman gave him a robe on which she had painted a dream which she made the robe magical and made anyone who wore it invisible. The warrior gave him a magical spear that would pierce anything, and a magical shield that would ward off anything, and a magical club that would break anything. The hunter showed him how to find anything he wanted. His mother made clothes of good deerskin and the young women put ornaments on them. While ornamenting his clothing, they sang love songs and Shaman conjured the ornaments (Ca Kina Wakan Kaga) so that they were magical. On the sides of his moccasins they put mountains so that he could step from hill to hill without touching the valleys; on the tops they put dragonflies so that he could escape all danger; on his leggings they put wolf tracks so that he would never grow weary; on his shirt they put the teepee circle so that he could find shelter anywhere.

He stood before the people, clothed in his magical garments, his shield on his back and his spear and club in his hands. His face was towards the rising Sun. Before him was his mother, on one side the Shaman, warrior, and hunter, and on the other, the old woman and the four young maidens. He said to his mother, "I will bring the Four Brothers to you." To the young women, "When I return I will take you four as my women." To the men, "What you have told me I will use to release the Four Brothers." Then turning his face towards the setting Sun he said to the old woman, "I go."

Then the old woman threw the robe about him and he was seen no more, but there was a wind as if the Thunderbird flew towards the setting sun. His mother fell on her face as if dead, but the people heard a voice high in the air, clear and loud like the voices of the cranes when they fly towards the region of the pines, and this is what it said: "A stone shall free the Four Brothers."

When the Stone Boy went from the people, he stepped from hill to hill more swiftly than the stars (meteors) fall at night. From each hill he looked carefully into the valley so that he saw all there was in every valley, but he saw nothing of the Four Brothers until he came to the high hills far towards the setting sun.

In the valley there was much game of every kind and in one he found a stone knife that he knew belonged to the eldest brother. In another valley he found a stone arrowhead that he knew belonged to the next eldest brother. In a third, he found a stone axe that he knew belonged to the next youngest brother, and in a fourth he found a stone bone breaker that he knew belonged to the youngest brother. Then he knew he was on the right road to find the Brothers and looked carefully into each valley.

Near the mountains he saw a valley that was barren, with nothing in it but a stone, a tree, and a little brown hill from which he saw smoke rising. He took off his robe and sat down to watch this. Soon a huge coyote, larger than a buffalo, came out of the hill and began to jump up very high and yelp very loud. Then the stone began to roll and bump about and the tree began to move from place to place. The stone went to a pool of water and took a drink.

The Stone Boy continued to watch, and soon a growl like thunder came from the hills beyond. The coyote, when he heard this growl, jumped very high and fast and yelped and yelled; the tree moved from place to place, and a little woman came out of the hill and looked towards the growling. Soon a huge bear as large as a cloud came over the hills. He walked upright like a man and held some people in his forepaws, and his growl sounded like thunder. He came into the valley and held the people up to the tree. The Stone Boy saw that each branch of the tree was a snake. These snakes bit the people as the bear held them up so that they were paralyzed.

When they were still as if they were dead, the bear threw them down on the hard smooth ground and the stone rolled over them and flattened them so that they were like dried buffalo skins.

Thus the little old woman laid them on the little brown hill and the Stone Boy saw that the hill was made of flattened people piled one on top of another. When the people had all been placed on the hill, the coyote sniffed towards the hill where the Stone Boy stood and jumped and yelled. Then he sniffed and jumped again; he sniffed very hard, jumped very high, and yelped very loud and the little old woman pointed to that hill and the bear growled and came to it. But the Stone Boy put on his robe and stepped to another hill. The bear looked foolish and said, "That must have been a Thunderbird (Wakinyan), a Winged God."

Thus the coyote sniffed towards the hill where the Stone Boy stood and again jumped up and down and the tree walked that way and the stone came also. Then they growled like very heavy thunder and came creeping towards the hill, watching everything closely, but when he got near, the Stone Boy stepped to another hill. Then the bear was afraid, and he ran back to the little hill, whining and whimpering, for he thought it was a Thunderbird. Then the little old woman came out of the hill, and the coyote yelped and jumped up and down and ran around and around, and branches of the tree squirmed and licked their tongues and hissed like a great wind. The stone jumped up and down, and every time it came down, it shook the earth.

Then the Stone Boy stood up and took off his robe and jeered at them and mocked them. They saw him. The old woman screamed and the coyote yelped louder than ever and jumped up and down, and the tree walked towards him, every snake hissing louder. The stone rolled and tumbled towards him and the bear came very fast towards him growling like a Thunder Cloud. When the bear was very close, he raised his paw to strike, but the Stone Boy shot one of the arrows through his heart and he fell dead.

Then the coyote came jumping up and down. Every time he jumped up, he went higher and higher, and when he was near enough he jumped up so as to come down on the Stone Boy, but the Stone Boy set his spear on the ground, and when the coyote came down the spear ran through his heart and killed him. Then the stone came rolling and tumbling and smashing everything in its path. When it was about to roll over the Stone Boy and smash him, he raised his war club and struck it a mighty blow and broke it to pieces.

The tree could not walk up the hill, so the Stone Boy went down into the valley, and when he came near the tree the branches began to strike him. But he held up the shield the warrior had given him, and when one of the snakes branches would strike it, its teeth would break off and its head would be smashed. So the Stone Boy danced about the tree and sang and shouted until every branch had smashed itself to death against the shield.

The little old woman then went into the little hill, and the Stone Boy came near it and cried, "Ho, old woman, come out." But the old woman said,, "My friend, I am a weak old woman. Have pity on me and come into my teepee."

The Stone Boy saw that the hill was a strange kind of teepee. He found the door, went in, and the old woman said, "My friend, I am a weak old woman, but you are welcome to my teepee. I will get you something to eat and drink." The Stone Boy noticed that her tongue was forked, so he was very wary and watched her closely.

She said, "My friend, you must be tired. Lie down and rest while I get food for you." The Stone Boy laid down and the old woman passed close, saying to him, "The meat is behind you." As she leaned over him she stabbed him over the heart, but her stone knife broke off when it struck him.

She said, "My friend, I stumbled and fell on you." The Stone Boy said, "I will sit up, so you will not stumble over me." So she said, "My friend, sit near the center of the teepee, so I can go about without stumbling over you."

So the Stone Boy sat near the center of the lodge, and the old woman moved about him. As she passed him she struck him on the head with a war club, but it only bounced off without hurting him, so she said, "My friend, you must be hungry. I will make soup for you." She made soup with bad medicine in it and gave it to the Stone Boy, who drank it.

The old woman said, "Ho, you are the one I hate. I am Iya, the evil spirit. I hate all people. I have given you that which will destroy you. You have swallowed poison. It will kill you. I am Iya the evil one. I know whom you seek. You were hunting for your mother's brothers. They are there in that teepee. They are like tanned skins. You will soon die and I will make a tanned skin of you. I must have a living stone to flatten you out and I must find it. The living stone was my master. He is the only one I feared. He is the only one that could hurt me. No one else can do me any harm. His only relative is a living stone. He is now my master and none other. But you will die from the poison I have given you and I will sing your death song."

She sang:

A young man would be wise.
A young man would be brave.

He left the places he knew.
He came to strange places.

He came to death valley.
He came to Iya's teepee.

He slew Iya's son, the coyote.
He slew Iya's daughter, the snake tree.

He broke the living stone.
He broke Iya's master.

Iya will be revenged on him.
Iya will see him die.

He slew my friend the bear.
Iya will laugh and see him die.

Then the Stone Boy said, "May I also sing a song?" Iya said, "Ho, sing what you will. It is your death song and it is music that will make my heart glad."

The living stone was Iya's master.
The living stone had but one relation.

He had a son that was little.
A pebble that was white as snow.

Iya feared the pebble and stole it.
Feared it because it was white.

Iya carried it into a far away country.
Iya threw it from him on a hilltop.

Where it would not be nourished.
Where it was not be life warmed.

He thought no one would find it.
He thought it would be there forever.

A woman born mysterious.
Found this pebble mysterious.

She gave to it the warmth of life.
The son of the living stone.

The wisest Shaman taught him wisdom.
The bravest warrior taught him bravery.

The oldest woman taught him cunning.
The best of women taught him kindness.

The people taught him justice.
To strive for the right against evil.

He was charmed from harm by the Shaman.
He was armed against evil by the warrior.

On his robe was the dream of the old woman.
On his feet was the magic of the young woman.

Thus he came to death's valley.
Thus he came to Iya's teepee.

He slew Iya's friend, the bear.
Because he enticed the people away.

He slew Iya's son, the coyote.
Because he did evil only.

He slew Iya's daughter, the snake tree,
because her faults were many.

Iya's knife would not harm him.
Iya's club would not kill him.

Iya's broth would not kill him.
It only makes him warm and strong.

I had enabled you threw away.
I am the Stone Boy, your master.

Then Iya said, "How shall I know you are to be my master?" The Stone Boy said, " Do my bidding or will punish you." Then Iya said, "I am a weak old woman. Have pity on me and do not punish me." The Stone Boy said, "Your tongue is forked, and you do not tell the truth. You are not a woman. You are an evil old man. You have pity on no one, but do evil to everyone. Tell me, where are my mother's brothers?" Iya said ,"I do not know. I was only boasting when I said I knew where they were. Have pity on me. Do not make it hard for me." Then the Stone Boy said, "I will have no pity on you. Tell me where my mother's brothers are." Iya said, "I do not know."

Then the Stone Boy seized him by the foot and placed it on the ground and trod on it, and Iya's foot was flattened like a piece of dried skin and he howled with pain. But the Stone Boy demanded he tell where his mother's brothers were, and Iya declared that he did not know. Then the Stone Boy flattened his other foot in the same way, and Iya sobbed and cried with pain and said he would tell all to the Stone Boy if he would not punish him any further, for Iya recognized that the Stone Boy was truly his master.

Iya said: "In ancient times, I found game plentiful in the valleys below here, and good hunters and brave men came here to hunt it. These good men could not be made to do evil at their homes, so I could not do them mischief. So I made a bargain with your father, the living stone, and with the great bear and bought my sons and daughter with me and we all lived here in this valley. (Iya was a giant; he fought with the living stone. The stone conquered him and became his master. He kept Iya with nothing to eat until he grew smaller and became a little old person.)

"The bargain was that the bear would go out among the game, and when a good man came to hunt, the bear would show himself and, being so big, the hunters would chase him until they came where they could see my son, who would jump up and down and scare them so that they would fall down with no strength. Then the bear would take them in his arms and bring to my daughter, who would sting them so they would be paralyzed. Then the living stone would roll on them and flatten them out like skins and I would heap them onto my teepee poles. As they were alive, this would always be a torment for them. In this way I could do mischief to good men.

"We often heard of the four men who lived alone and did woman's work and who never did evil to anyone, so that I could not torment them. But they would not hunt or go on the war path, and we thought they would never come within our power. So I determined to get a woman into their teepee that it might do something evil, but I could not get an ordinary woman among them. Then I tried to break off a branch from my daughter, the snake tree and put it into their teepee, but the branches would not break and the only way I could get a part of my daughter was by digging out a part of the heart of the tree. This I did and placed it near the teepee of the four brothers so that when one of them went to get wood he would step on it and stick it into his toe. These man were so good that when they cared for this child it grew up to be a good woman -- as they were good men -- but I waited patiently, for when she grew to be a woman I knew they would not live as they had before. When she was a woman they came to hunt game for her, and the bear enticed them and they were caught and flattened and are now tormented on my teepee poles.

"When I threw the white pebble away, I knew that no ordinary woman could nourish it into life and growth, and when your mother grew up to be a woman, I did not think of being a mysterious woman who could give life and growth to the pebble. So my own evil has brought the punishment on me, for I know that you are my master and that you will not let me do evil any more. But those who now lie on teepee poles will still be tormented."

Then the Stone Boy said, "Tell me: how can these people that are on your teepee poles be restored to their natural condition?" Iya said, "I will not." The Stone Boy said, "I am your master. Tell me or I will punish you." Then Iya said, "Remember, I am your grandfather, and do not punish me." The Stone Boy said, "I broke my own father in pieces because he was evil. Do you think I would spare you because you are my grandfather?" Iya said, "I will not tell you."

Then the Stone Boy said, "Give me your hand." He took Iya's hand and trod on it and it was flattened like a dried skin and Iya howled with pain. Then the Stone Boy said, "Tell me or I will flatten your other hand." and Iya said, "I will tell you." "You must skin the bear and coyote and stretch a skins over poles so as to make a tight teepee. Then you must gather all the pieces of the broken living stone. You must make a fire of the wood from the snake tree and heat the stones is over this fire, and placed them in teepee. Then get one of the flattened people off the poles of my teepee and place it in the teepee you have built. Then place the hot stones in the teepee and pour water over the stones. When the steam rises into the flattened person, he will be as he was before the bear enticed him."

Then the Stone Boy did as he was told, but the skins of the bear and the coyote would not make a full sized teepee, so he made it low and round on top. When he made a fire of the snake tree, the branches were so fat that one would heat all the stones red hot. He had plenty of fuel to heat the stones as often has he wished. So he placed the flattened people in the sweat house and steamed them and they became men as they were before they were enticed by the bear.

He did not know who his mother's brothers were, so he took the arrow he had found and called to all and asked them whose arrow it was. One man said it was his. He told him stand to one side. He took the stone knife he had found and asked whose it was. A man said it was his, and he told him to stand to one side. He then took the plant seed dice he had found and asked whose it were. One man said it was his, and he told him to stand to one side. Then he told the men he had asked to stand aside to look at each other. They did so, and when they had looked at each other they embraced each other, and the Stone Boy knew they were brothers.

Then the Stone Boy told them story of the four men, of the birth of his mother and how the four man went away and never came back. Then the men said, "We are those four men." The Stone Boy knew that they were his mother's brothers, so he told them the story of his own birth, and they said, "We believe you, because we know the birth of your mother." Then he told them of his preparation to come for them, of his coming and his fight with bear, the coyote, the stone, and the snake tree, and how he was the master of Iya. They said, "We believe you, because the bear did entice us and the coyote did jump up and down and the snake bit us and the stone did roll over and make as flat like skins and the old woman did spread us on her teepee and we were tormented."

Then the Stone Boy counseled with them as to what he should do to Iya. They advised him to make him flat like a skin, but the Stone Boy said, "There is no snake tree to bite him." He came back to Iya and said, "You have been very evil, but now I am your master and I shall punish you for all the evil you have done so that you always be in torment as you have kept all these people." Iya was a great coward and he begged the Stone Boy to spare him and not punish him. But the Stone Boy said, "I shall flatten you like skin and spread you on a pole."

Then Iya said, "I am Iya, the giant, and I will grow so big that you cannot flatten me." He began to grow and grew larger and larger so that he was a great giant. But the Stone Boy began to trample on him. Beginning at his feet, which he had already flattened, he trampled on his legs, so that Iya fell to his knees; he trampled on his thighs so that Iya fell to his buttocks; he trampled on his hips so that great floods of water ran from him. This water was bitter and salty and it soaked into the Earth, and where it comes out in springs or lakes it makes the water very bad and bitter.

Then he trampled his belly, and Iya vomited great quantities of cherry stones, and the Stone Boy said to him, "What are these cherry stones?" and Iya said, "They are the people that I have sucked in with my breath when I went about the Earth as a giant." The Stone Boy said, "How can I make these people as they were when you sucked them in with your breath?" Iya said, "Make a fire without smoke." So the Stone Boy got very dry cottonwood and made a fire and when it was burned to coals Iya said, "Get some of the hair from the great bear's skin." He got hair from the great bear, and Iya said, "Put the hair on the fire." And he put it on the fire. Then there rose a great white smoke, and it was like the smoke from wild sage branches and leaves. Then Iya said, "Blow this smoke on the cherry stones." The Stone Boy did so, and Iya said, "This drives away all my power to do these people any harm." Iya said, "Get the hair of many women." The Stone Boy did so then there was a thick blue smoke like the smoke of sweet grass and Iya said, "This gives you power to do what you wish to these people."

The Stone Boy said to the people, "Be as you were before Iya sucked you in with his breath." Every cherry stone arose. They were transformed into more women and children, so that there were a great many people there. These people were all very hungry, so the Stone Boy said to Iya, "What shall I give these people to eat?" Iya replied. "Give them the flesh of the great bear." So he cut off a piece of the flesh of the great bear and gave it to a woman. It grew to be a large piece, and this woman cut it in two and gave half of it to another woman. Immediately each of these pieces grew large. Each time a piece was given away it grew large. Then the women built fires and cooked the meat and all feasted and were happy and sang songs.

The people spoke many different languages and could not understand one another, but the Stone Boy could speak to each one in his own language. He addressed some in their own tongue, "Where was your place?" They replied, "Over the mountains." He said to them, "Go to your people." As he said this to everyone, he gave to the oldest woman of each people a piece of the flesh from the great bear, so that they had plenty to eat while they traveled. Then the Stone Boy said to his mother's brothers, "Now we will go back to your sister, to my mother, but before we go I will destroy Iya so that he may do no more mischief or hurt the people."

He trod on Iya's chest and his breath rushed out of his mouth and nostrils like a mighty wind and then whirled and twisted, breaking down trees, tearing up grass, throwing water from the lake, and even piling the rocks and Earth over the carcasses of the coyote and the snake tree, so that the Thunderbird came rushing through the air to find out what all this tumult was about. With his cloud shield he rushed into this great whirlwind, and while the lightening spit and flashed from his eyes, he fought the whirlwind and carried it away into the sky.

Then the Stone Boy said to Iya, "I will now tread your head and your arms out flat like a dried skin and you shall remain forever here in his evil valley where there is no tree, nor grass, nor water, and no living thing will ever come near you. The Sun shall burn you and the cold shall freeze you and you shall feel and think and be hungry and thirsty, but no one shall come near you."

Iya grew so large that he almost lay across the valley. His hands were upon the hill where the Stone Boy first showed himself. When the Stone Boy told him his fate, his hands grasped for something, and he felt the Stone Boy's robe. This he quickly threw over himself and immediately he became invisible. But the Stone Boy saw what he was doing and jumped quickly to trample the breath out of Iya, his mouth gaped wide open. He got the robe over his head before Stone Boy could get his feet on him. When the

Stone Boy did trample Iya, he stepped into his mouth, so Iya closed his jaws like a trap and caught both of the Stone Boy's feet between his teeth.

Iya could not hurt the Stone Boy, but he held the feet and very tightly between his teeth, and when the Stone Boy drew out one foot, he closed still closer on the other so that when that one was dragged out, the moccasin was left in Iya's mouth and was invisible and could not be found.

Trouble no more about their religion;
respect others in their view,
and demand that they respect yours.

Chief Tecumseh

First Creator and Lone Man Version 1
(A Mandan Legend)

It is our custom to tell an old-time story when the corn is ripe. We have a man called Lone Man. As he was walking along he came to himself. He stood and thought. A pipe was laying in front of him, over his head flew a raven. And his sang a song which said, "Where did I come from?" He thought, "Where did I come from? How did I happen to come here?" The Earth about him was Sandy and he could plainly see his own tracks, so he followed them back to see where he came from. He came to a wet spot, then farther on to a great water, beside which was a plant with spotted leaves. A Buffalo Bug was jumping about in the sand. The plant said, "I am your mother, it was I that bore you; that is your father." And the Weed-mother told Lone Man that he was born to arrange matters on the Earth. "Go back to the wet spot and there you will find a tall Weed. This is your pipe. I am just a Weed, this is all I am for. If anyone has a sore eye or stomach trouble, let him take me and boil me up for medicine. Go ahead and create things in the world." When he came to himself he had a Wolf blanket and a cane with feathers tied to the end. He came to the wet spot, and there grew a tall Tobacco Weed and around it buzzed a Tobacco Fly -- buzz, buzz. The bug said, "I am a blowing your tobacco plant -- use it to smoke." Again he sang the same song -- "Where did I come from?" And he pulled up the tobacco plant.

As he was trotting along at a gentle pace, another man came up suddenly. The two argued as to which was the eldest. They agreed: "You lie here and I there and the first one that gets up will be the youngest." Lone Man said he would leave his cane standing as the other turned about and laid down, and Lone Man sang the same song -- "Where did I come from?" He went on his way, and traveled over the whole world from one end to the other. Then he thought of his cane, and returning to the spot where it stood, he found it tottering and ready to fall. Grass grew where the other lay. He said, "This fellow can never get up again!" He took his cane and it became like new and he sang his song and was about to trot away again when the other man got up from the heap of dust where his body had been and said, "I told you that I was older than you!"

The two traveled to create the world. They looked for mud, but there was sand alone. They came to a great lake where there were two Mud Hens, a male and female. They called them over and made them their servants, and the Mud Hens dived and brought mud, and the men made all creatures. They would throw the mud in the air and at once it became a bird. One bird had no place to go, so it flew over to the stony places and became a Nighthawk. Another stuck its head into the red paint, saying it was hungry, and when it pulled its head out, the head was red, so they said it should have a hard time to get a living out of rotten trees. This was the Woodpecker.

They made many kinds of different birds and animals and at last a grandmother frog came and said, "You are making too many animals; we must make death so that the first ones may pass away and new ones come." The two said, "You have nothing to say about our business!" And they picked up a stone and heat grandmother frog on the back. This is why her legs spread out so. This is how death started, and the child of grandmother frog was the first to die. Grandmother frog came to the men and said "I am sorry! Let us take it back and have no deaths!" But the men said, "No, it is impossible; it must be so."

The two said, "Let us improve the Earth -- it is all sand!" So they took the mud that was left and Lone Man took his lump and smoothed it over the Earth and the Earth was flat. First Creator took a little bit and put it here and there and formed hills and bluffs. Lone Man used his cane and leveled the north side of the Earth and made lakes. The First Creator's idea was that when the snow flies there should be rough land and trees and springs to protect men and animals from the cold. First Creator made nothing but Buffalo to roam over the land and in every herd he made a White Buffalo and he said that this White One should be precious. From the East this way Only Man created and First Creator created the South side of the Earth. Thus it has been told from generation to generation.

After the creation Lone Man was never seen again. First Creator turned him into a Coyote and from him came the Coyote today. He never knew where he came from.

Why not teach school children more of the wholesome proverbs and legends of our people? That we killed game only for food, not for fun... Tell your children of the friendly acts of the Indians to the white people who first settled here. Tell them of our leaders and heroes and their deeds... Put in your history books the Indian's part in the World War. Tell how the Indian fought for a country of which he was not a citizen, for a flag to which he had no claim, and for a people who treated him unjustly. We ask this, Chief, to keep sacred the memory of our people.

Grand Council Fire of American Indians to the Mayor of Chicago, 1927

Crow Necklace and His Medicine Ceremony
(A Gros Ventre Legend)

There was a party of Gros Ventre Indians who went out for a hunt from Knife River where the old camp was, and while they were hunting, the Assiniboins came and attacked the hunters. Some got away and were saved. A young man among them looked for his sister and could not find her. So he trailed them to their camp. This man was an Assiniboin who had been a little boy captured by the Gros Ventre and made a slave. The girl called him brother, but was not really related to him. When all was quiet at night he went through the camp to look for his sister. He came to a big teepee and heard talking.

Looking through a hole, he saw two men wounded whom he recognized as his own brothers. Now he had shot two Assiniboin in the conflict (and he recognized these two as the ones he shot). Drawing his robe over his head, he entered and sat down beside their father, who was his father too. The wounded men told their father to fill his pipe and smoke with the stranger. The boy had not forgotten his own language, so he spoke to the old man and said, "Father, it is I." When he told what had happened to him, the father put his hands about his neck and fainted; the mother did the same. When he told them it was he who had shot the two brothers, they all laughed over it. He told them that he was looking for his sister, and the wounded men advised the father to call in the chiefs and tell them about her. So the chiefs arranged not to move camp for four days, but to have a feast and call together all the slaves taken from the Gros Ventre and let them eat. Then they had a dance called the Scalp-Dance, but the sister was not there. According to the old custom, slaves are supposed to belong to the tribe by which they are captured, so the slaves too got up and danced with them. All the slaves knew the young man. They called him "Crow Necklace."

Before the four days were passed he said to the slaves, "Go steal some moccasins and dry meat and one of these nights we will run away." On the last of the four nights they were all prepared. They stole sinew and cut pieces of Buffalo hide from the tents for moccasins. It was storming when they left - young women, old, and children, the young women carrying the children on their backs - and they ran North instead of East in the direction from which they came. Coming to a dry lake, they laid down in the deep grass and the snow covered them. Meanwhile, the Assiniboin discovered their absence and tracked after them but could not find them. They came to the lake but, seeing nothing of them, went home except one who stood looking. Crow Necklace crept up and killed him and took his scalp.

That night they went until daylight, traveling North-East until they came to another dry lake thick with grass. There they stayed all day. Four days they traveled in the night and hid all day. By this time they were up at the head waters. From there they came around toward the Missouri River and came out at a place we call "Timber Coulee." At that time it was full of timber. Crow Necklace was about to push down an old tree which had an Owl's nest on top. An old Owl said, "Don't push that tree or my young ones will get cold. We are the ones who have helped you get around to your home again. It will be best for you to go back to your own tribe: there you will find a chief's daughter waiting to marry you." So when they wanted him to marry some of the women he refused and said, "No! the young ones are my sisters and the old ones are my mothers. The Owl directed him, "After leaving this place, go directly to the Short Missouri to camp, then on to Wood-Trap (right across the river West from here). Here all the Spirits will set traps to catch all kinds of wild animals for you to eat. When you get there, build a teepee out in the bush. Go inside and do not go out, and they will bring you meat themselves." So they did this - fixed up nice and went in. Outside they could hear the noise of butchering going on around them.

When the noise ceased they went out and found meat cut up or wrapped in hides and laid up on scaffolds. The Owl told Crow Necklace that they were now not far from the tribe - at the next move they would reach home. The next day they moved until they came to a high hill. Crow Necklace fixed up a skull and painted their faces black. As they approached, they saw a woman crying on top of a hill and someone pointed her out to Cow Necklace; it was his sister. He called to her, and when she saw him she fainted. Then the whole camp came out to meet them and everybody made much of Crow Necklace. He told the story of their adventures and brought food for them to eat.

All the hides he had asked to have tanned in order to make Medicine after he got back home. Among them was a White Buffalo hide. So after he had married a chief's daughter as had been foretold, he made Medicine in order to understand all the mysterious beings and leave out none of them. And that cost him everything he had prepared - a hundred moccasins, a hundred robes, a hundred blankets - everything in hundreds.

The Story of Hungry Wolf
(An Assiniboin Legend)

A young man and his wife were up hunting in the breaks North of Little Missouri, back by Kildeer Mountains. The man camped there with his wife. He was successful as a hunter, and his wife cured the hides and fried strips of jerked meat. One night he told her to pack up everything, as the next day they would be leaving. Early the next morning he went out to get some fresh meat for the journey and returned with parts of a Rocky Mountain Sheep and its hide, which the people regard as very valuable. He found the packages on the scaffold just as he had left them, but his wife and dog were gone.

Circling about the tent he found no trace, but the fourth day he found a few tracks of men. With the tracks of men were the tracks of his wife and dog heading South. He went back to the camp and pounded the meat and roasted the fattest meat and stored it away in bags to eat on the way, then he followed the trail. The fugitives hid their trail by spreading out and then coming together again, so that the tracks were hard to follow. Thus he followed a party which he judged to consist of twelve persons. When he came to Looks-Like-A-Chicken-Tail butte, he turned South-West and saw smoke rising from a camp. He waited till sunset, then he walked into the camp. There he stood for a while, considering. He covered his head with his robe, carrying bows and arrows under his robe in case of attack. He could see young men walking about engaged in courting. As he went from tent to tent listening for signs of his wife, their dog ran out from a tent and jumped about his master. He gave it meat. The dog returned to the tent, whined, wagged its tail and ran out again to its master. He went and stood in the doorway. Within he could see his wife sitting. An old woman came in, and to his surprise his wife spoke to him in Gros Ventres. She was an old woman who had also been taken prisoner and had lived among the enemy until she was old.

He surveyed the situation of the camp. On the outskirts was a ravine where a spring had made a small pond. A trail led down to this pond, made by the woman going after water. Beside the pond grew Beaver Grass, long and fine, right down to the water's edge. There he hid, hoping that when his wife came down to get water, they might plan an escape. His plan was to start in the night, go Westward toward the mountains, and come back home. In the morning a stream of women came down to the water. At noon fewer came. In the early afternoon he saw the dog coming down the bank wagging its tail. His wife came to the edge of the spring and, standing on a stone, leaned over to dip water. He said "Stay just where you are, my own heart. I heard you talking last night with the old woman. My plan is for you to come out here when everyone is asleep. The people will expect us to go back to our old camp, so we will go towards the mountains and live on game on the way home. Afterwards we will go back and get our packages at the camp,"

He laid behind the grass. In the evening after the woman had left who came down to the water, the men came down and encircled the pond. They overpowered him, took away his bow and arrows and carried him away to a tent and gave him food. His wife came and looked into the tent. He said, "I believe it is you who have betrayed me."

They dug two holes in a circle, set in two posts, lanced his muscles next to the bone at wrists and ankles, stretched his arms and legs to the posts; then they scalped him, and tying the scalp to a long pole, they sent out drummers and all came out and danced the victory dance and carried his scalp about on the pole. They brought firewood and made a pile of it before and behind him, intending to burn him; but just then an old man came out who seemed to have authority, and stopped the dancing and made signs towards the Sun, but his words were unintelligible. The old Gros Ventre woman came to him and said, "My dear, it is all your wife's fault. You communicated with her when she went down to get water. When she returned she told the camp that there was a Corn Man down in the water-hole. I was taken away when young by these people and have been here ever since. I married and have children and grandchildren and hence been contented to live among them. When they brought the Gros Ventre woman here, as she was one of our tribe. I went over to her tent to comfort her. It was your wife who advised that you be captured and tortured to death. You cannot expect a woman to keep a secret. The man who spoke to the people told them that when we fight and kill an enemy we kill him quickly. He said, "The great God in the heavens is looking down upon us. If you burn this man, that Great Spirit will some day avenge this deed. He will punish us. Let us wait and see what will happen."

The next day when the people broke camp, some came over and pierced his eyes; then they left him and went away. For four days he remained hanging. On the fourth day towards dusk he heard an Owl hooting. He came nearer and hooted again. He could hear the grass rustling as from a man walking close to him. The steps stopped in front of him and a man said, "My son, the hooting of the Owl was myself. I have come to see what I can do to restore your sight." He heard him spitting on his hands and rubbing his palms together. The man told him to look up, and he rubbed the palms of his hands over his eyes, and his eyesight was restored. The man told him, "Fear not, the torture from which you were suffering has been caused by your wife. But you shall live and see your home again. You must stand and listen at daybreak when the Sun comes over the hill and you will hear the Earth trembling and the sound of something falling to Earth. That which you hear falling and whose vibration you feel is white clay, which is being made for you in the sky and dropped from the sky to Earth. You will find it near Red Grass butt beside Knife River. When you get home, when you give a dance, let the Grandma society clean a lodge site and pile the grass in the center as a symbol of your standing here. Strip a cane in four places as a symbol of the four days you have stood here without food and water. It will be a token of long life and prosperity. Give another such cane to a brother or some relative. The two canes are symbols of the two torture posts. There shall be a circle for the Wolf society and the old scouts shall circle around you. Take one winder to prepare all the articles for the dance. Ask all your friends and relatives to help you. They shall make arrows and give them as payment to the scouts who sing and tell their exploits as they shall give them to their sons and young relatives to use against those who torture you. Next year you will find these same people camping here, and you shall kill a hundred of them. You shall capture this old Gros Ventre woman and your wife. Save their lives, but do not make the woman your wife again. You shall marry the daughters of your chief. Teach your warriors to use in the battle shields made of Buffalo hide hardened by burning with hot stones.

The Owl Man told him that in the morning he would see Wolf-Of-The-Sunset dancing with his warriors. He must watch their dress and learn their songs and make this dance a part of his Mystery. In the morning Wolf-Of-The-Sunset came with his warriors, who were a pack of Wolves. They freed him and took him into their company by the name of Hungry Wolf. The scouts come in the rear. The Raven as he flies over the country seeing all that is going on is like the scout. It was the Raven who had told the Owl how the man was being tortured and had reported it to Wolf-Of-The-Sunset. That is why the two men who led the Wolf Dance and impersonate Wolf-Of-The-Sunset and Hungry Wolf wear Raven feathers. Just as the Wolves do for the "fasters" in the dance, so the Wolves came that day, removed the rawhides that bound him and gave him the feast of fat of the Buffalo to eat. They said, "This will drive away the pain of the torture. When your people kill a Buffalo, after skinning the breastbone, they must take a mouthful of the fat, and whatever their sickness this will cure it." They took fat and anointed his wounds in his arms and feet and on the forehead. They daubed him with white clay all over and then, as a sign of healing, they made scratches with their fingernails in the clay on his calves, his forearm, and on his forehead, thus leaving the clay in streaks. This white clay is used in the Wolf ceremony. The heap in the center of the clearing is the symbol of his torture. When they dance about , they must go over to the right side (and dance from the right to the left) in order to insure long life and prosperity; if they start from the left, it is a sign of misery. So when people smoke, the pipe is handed to the extreme right of the circle and then handed around.

The Wolves told him to follow them. When he got over the divide, he found a Buffalo butchered and blood and kidney, liver and guts, laid aside from the Buffalo's head, sang a song, and his torn scalp was healed and the hair turned to the color of his own hair. Thus he reached home, Then he climbed up to his old lodge, face to the West, and said, "Hee-hay!" (which signifies "Listen!"). He spoke to the Wolves of the West and said, "This winter I shall have bedding (Buffalo hides) scraped for you and shall bring the Wolves into my lodge (meaning warriors) in order to conquer my enemies." Taking hunters and Dogs, he returned to his old camp and brought back his bundles. He placed food in those lodges where the societies met and in return they gave arrows and other things for the ceremony. He sent one of his sisters to the chief's lodge and asked for the hand of the chiefs two daughters in marriage.

During the winter he instructed the Wolves in the scout songs he had learned from the Wolves. In the summer he sent for the white clay and had the dance performed. After this he called for the young men through the announcer and for the old men who had endurance and speed and provided them with moccasins and provisions for the war path. On the outskirts of the village the warriors assembled. When they reached the butte, he was told that this was the place to mine the bright red ochre which is to be found there in pockets. Since he had too many scouts, he selected from the forty-five the fourteen who were the fastest runners. They had to run one by one between the two goals while the rest in the center tried to catch them.

This is called "running by." If anyone was caught before he reached the opposite goal, he was put out. They went on and sent out scouts ahead. They reported a hundred and fifty tents. There were 2500 persons in the village. They got close to camp, whooped, and attacked at daybreak. After a hundred warriors had been killed, he gave the signal to stop by waving his robe in the air. No women or children were killed, or any old people. The old Gros Ventre woman and the young man's wife were taken. The old woman was allowed to go back to the tribe; the wife was brought back to the village. No one would marry her, and it was she who introduced harlotry.

In the village they danced the greatest village dance ever known. Hungry Wolf lived to old age and had children and grandchildren. The mystery he conferred upon his son, and so it was handed down from generation to generation.

. . everything on the earth has a purpose, every disease an herb to cure it, and every person a mission. This is the Indian theory of existence.

Mourning Dove (Christine Quintasket), Salish

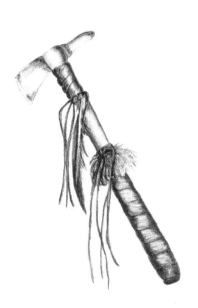

Origin of the Sweat Lodge
(A Blackfoot Legend)

The Piegan tribe was southernmost at the headwaters of the Missouri River in Montana, a sub-tribe belonging to the Siksika Indians of North Saskatchewan in Canada. Piegans were of the Algonquian linguistic family, but warlike toward most of their neighboring tribes, since they had horses for raiding and were supplied with guns and ammunition by their Canadian sources. Piegans also displayed hostility toward explorers and traders. Several smallpox epidemics decimated their population. Now they are gathered on reservations on both sides of the border.

A girl of great beauty, the Chief's daughter, was worshipped by many young handsome men of the Piegan tribe. But she would not have any one of them for her husband.

One young tribesman was very poor and his face was marked with an ugly scar. Although he saw rich and handsome men of his tribe rejected by the Chief's daughter, he decided to find out if she would have him for her husband. When she laughed at him for even asking, he ran away toward the south in shame.

After traveling several days, he dropped to the ground, weary and hungry, and fell asleep. From the heavens, Morning-Star looked down and pitied the young unfortunate youth, knowing his trouble.

To Sun and Moon, his parents, Morning-Star said, "There is a poor young man lying on the ground with no one to help him. I want to go after him for a companion."

"Go and get him," said his parents.

Morning-Star carried the young man, Scarface, into the sky. Sun said, "Do not bring him into my lodge yet, for he smells ill. Build four sweat lodges."

When this was done, Sun led Scarface into the first sweat lodge. He asked Morning-Star to bring a hot coal on a forked stick. Sun then broke off a bit of sweet grass and placed it upon the hot coal. As the incense arose Sun began to sing, "Old Man is coming in with his body; it is sacred," repeating it four times.

Sun passed his hands back and forth through the smoke and rubbed them over the face, left arm, and side of Scarface. Sun repeated the ceremony on the boy's right side, purifying him and removing the odors of earthly people.

Sun took Scarface into the other three sweat lodges, performing the same healing ceremony. The body of Scarface changed color and he shone like a yellow light.

Using a soft feather, Sun brushed it over the youth's face, magically wiping away the scar. With a final touch to the young man's long, yellow hair, Sun caused him to look exactly like Morning-Star. The two young men were led by Sun into his own lodge and placed side by side in the position of honor.

"Old Woman," called the father. "Which is your son?"

Moon pointed to Scarface, "That one is our son."

"You do not know your own child," answered Sun.

"He is not our son. We will call him Mistaken-for-Morning-Star," as they all laughed heartily at the mistake.

The two boys were together constantly and became close companions. One day, they were on an adventure when Morning-Star pointed out some large birds with very long, sharp beaks.

"Foster-Brother, I warn you not to go near those dangerous creatures," said Morning-Star. "They killed my other brothers with their beaks."

Suddenly the birds chased the two boys. Morning-Star fled toward his home, but Foster-Brother stopped, picking up a club and one by one struck the birds dead.

Upon reaching home, Morning-Star excitedly reported to his father what had happened. Sun made a victory song honoring the young hero. In gratitude for saving Morning-Star's life, Sun gave him the forked stick for lifting hot embers and a braid of sweet grass to make incense. These sacred elements necessary for making the sweat lodge ceremony were a gift of trust.

"And this my sweat lodge I give to you," said the Sun. Mistaken-for-Morning-Star observed very carefully how it was constructed, in his mind preparing himself to one day returning to earth.

When Scarface did arrive at his tribal village, all of his people gathered to see the handsome young man in their midst. At first, they did not recognize him as Scarface.

"I have been in the sky," he told them. "Behold me, Morning-Star looks just like this. The Sun gave me these things used in the sweat lodge healing ceremony. That is how I lost my ugly scar."

Scarface explained how the forked stick and sweet grass were used. Then he set to work showing his people how to make the sweat lodge. This is how the first medicine sweat lodge was built upon earth by the Piegan tribe.

Now that Scarface was so very handsome and brought such a great blessing of healing to his tribe, the Chief's beautiful daughter became his wife.

In remembrance of Sun's gift to Scarface and his tribe, the Piegans always make the sweat lodge healing ceremony an important part of their annual Sun Dance Celebration.

Conversation was never begun at once, nor in a hurried manner. No one was quick with a question, no matter how important, and no one was pressed for an answer. A pause giving time for thought was the truly courteous way of beginning and conducting a conversation. Silence was meaningful with the Lakota, and his granting a space of silence to the speech-maker and his own moment of silence before talking was done in the practice of true politeness and regard for the rule that "thought comes before speech."

Luther Standing Bear, Oglala Sioux Chief

Origin of the Medicine Lodge

In the earliest times there was no war. All the tribes were at peace. In those days there was a man who had a daughter, a very beautiful girl. Many young men wanted to marry her, but every time she was asked, she only shook her head and said she did not want a husband.

"How is this?" asked her father. "Some of these young men are rich, handsome, and brave."

"Why should I marry?" replied the girl. "I have a rich father and mother. Our lodge is good. The parfleches are never empty. There are plenty of tanned robes and soft furs for winter. Why worry me, then?"

The Raven Bearers held a dance; they all dressed carefully and wore their ornaments, and each one tried to dance the best. Afterwards some of them asked for this girl, but still she said no. Then the Bulls, the Kit-foxes, and others of the I-kun-uh'-kah-tsi held their dances, and all those who were rich, many great warriors, asked this man for his daughter, but to every one of them she said no. Then her father was angry, and said: "Why, now, this way? All the best men have asked for you, and still you say no. I believe you have a secret lover."

"Ah!" said her mother. "What shame for us should a child be born and our daughter still unmarried!" "Father, mother!" replied the girl, "pity me. I have no secret lover, but now hear the truth. That

Above Person, the Sun, told me, 'Do not marry any of those men, for you are mine; thus you shall be happy, and live to great age'; and again he said, 'Take heed. You must not marry. You are mine.'"

"Ah!" replied her father. "It must always be as he says." And they talked no more about it.

There was a poor young man, very poor. His father, mother, all his relations, had gone to the Sand Hills. He had no lodge, no wife to tan his robes or sew his moccasins. He stopped in one lodge today, and tomorrow he ate and slept in another; thus he lived. He was a good-looking young man, except that on his cheek he had a scar, and his clothes were always old and poor.

After those dances some of the young men met this poor Scarface, and they laughed at him, and said: "Why don't you ask that girl to marry you? You are so rich and handsome!" Scarface did not laugh; he replied: "Ah! I will do as you say. I will go and ask her." All the young men thought this was funny. They laughed a great deal. But Scarface went down by the river. He waited by the river, where the women came to get water, and by and by the girl came along. "Girl," he said, "wait. I want to speak with you. Not as a designing person do I ask you, but openly where the Sun looks down, and all may see."

"Speak then," said the girl.

"I have seen the days," continued the young man "You have refused those who are young, and rich, and brave. Now, today, they laughed and said to me, 'Why do you not ask her?' I am poor, very poor. I have no lodge, no food, no clothes, no robes and warm furs. I have no relations; all have gone to the Sand Hills; yet, now, today, I ask you, take pity, be my wife."

The girl hid her face in her robe and brushed the ground with the point of her moccasin, back and forth, back and forth; for she was thinking. After a time she said: "True. I have refused all those rich young men, yet now the poor one asks me, and I am glad. I will be your wife, and my people will be happy. You are poor, but it does not matter. My father will give you dogs. My mother will make us a lodge. My people will give us robes and furs. You will be poor no longer."

Then the young man was happy, and he started to kiss her, but she held him back, and said: "Wait! The Sun has spoken to me. He says I may not marry; that I belong to him. He says if I listen to him, I shall live to great age. But now I say: Go to the Sun. Tell him, 'She whom you spoke with heeds your words. She has never done wrong, but now she wants to marry. I want her for my wife.' Ask him to take that scar from your face. That will be his sign. I will know he is pleased. But if he refuses, or if you fail to find his lodge, then do not return to me."

"Oh!" cried the young man, "at first your words were good. I was glad. But now it is dark. My heart is dead. Where is that far-off lodge? where the trail, which no one yet has traveled?"

"Take courage, take courage!" said the girl; and she went to her lodge.

Scarface was very sad. He sat down and covered his head with his robe and tried to think what to do. After a while he got up, and went to an old woman who had been kind to him. "Pity me," he said. "I am very poor. I am going away now on a long journey. Make me some moccasins."

"Where are you going?" asked the old woman. "There is no war; we are very peaceful here."

"I do not know where I shall go," replied Scarface. "I am in trouble, but I cannot tell you now what it is."

So the old woman made him some moccasins, seven pairs, with parfleche soles, and also she gave him a sack of food, pemmican of berries, pounded meat, and dried back fat; for this old woman had a good heart. She liked the young man.

All alone, and with a sad heart, he climbed the bluffs and stopped to take a last look at the camp. He wondered if he would ever see his sweetheart and the people again. " Hai'-yu! Pity me, O Sun," he prayed, and turning, he started to find the trail.

For many days he traveled on, over great prairies, along timbered rivers and among the mountains, and every day his sack of food grew lighter; but he saved it as much as he could, and ate berries, and roots, and sometimes he killed an animal of some kind. One night he stopped by the home of a wolf. "Hai-yah!" said that one; "what is my brother doing so far from home?"

"Ah!" replied Scarface, "I seek the place where the Sun lives; I am sent to speak with him."

"I have traveled far," said the wolf. "I know all the prairies, the valleys, and the mountains, but I have never seen the Sun's home. Wait; I know one who is very wise. Ask the bear. He may tell you."

The next day the man traveled on again, stopping now and then to pick a few berries, and when night came he arrived at the bear's lodge.

"Where is your home?" asked the bear. "Why are you traveling alone, my brother?"

"Help me! Pity me!" replied the young man; "because of *her words* I seek the Sun. I go to ask him for her."

"I know not where he stops," replied the bear. "I have traveled by many rivers, and I know the mountains, yet I have never seen his lodge. There is some one beyond, that striped-face, who is very smart. Go and ask him."

The badger was in his hole. Stooping over, the young man shouted: "Oh, cunning striped-face! Oh, generous animal! I wish to speak with you."

"What do you want?" said the badger, poking his head out of the hole.

"I want to find the Sun's home," replied Scarface. "I want to speak with him."

"I do not know where he lives," replied the badger. "I never travel very far. Over there in the timber is a wolverine. He is always traveling around, and is of much knowledge. Maybe he can tell you."

Then Scarface went to the woods and looked all around for the wolverine, but could not find him. So he sat down to rest "Hai'-yu! Hai'-yu!" he cried. "Wolverine, take pity on me. My food is gone, my moccasins worn out. Now I must die."

"What is it, my brother?" he heard, and looking around, he saw the animal sitting near.

"She whom I would marry," said Scarface, "belongs to the Sun; I am trying to find where he lives, to ask him for her."

"Ah!" said the wolverine. "I know where he lives. Wait; it is nearly night. Tomorrow I will show you the trail to the big water. He lives on the other side of it."

Early in the morning, the wolverine showed him the trail, and Scarface followed it until he came to the water's edge. He looked out over it, and his heart almost stopped. Never before had any one seen such a big water. The other side could not be seen, and there was no end to it. Scarface sat down on the shore. His food was all gone, his moccasins worn out. His heart was sick. "I cannot cross this big water," he said. "I cannot return to the people. Here, by this water, I shall die."

Not so. His Helpers were there. Two swans came swimming up to the shore. "Why have you come here?" they asked him. "What are you doing? It is very far to the place where your people live."

"I am here," replied Scarface, "to die. Far away, in my country, is a beautiful girl. I want to marry her, but she belongs to the Sun. So I started to find him and ask for her. I have traveled many days. My food is gone. I cannot go back. I cannot cross this big water, so I am going to die."

"No," said the swans; "it shall not be so. Across this water is the home of that Above Person. Get on our backs, and we will take you there."

Scarface quickly arose. He felt strong again. He waded out into the water and lay down on the swans' backs, and they started off. Very deep and black is that fearful water. Strange people live there, mighty animals which often seize and drown a person. The swans carried him safely, and took him to the other side. Here was a broad hard trail leading back from the water's edge.

"Kyi" said the swans. "You are now close to the Sun's lodge. Follow that trail, and you will soon see it."

Scarface started up the trail, and pretty soon he came to some beautiful things, lying in it. There was a war shirt, a shield, and a bow and arrows. He had never seen such pretty weapons; but he did not touch them. He walked carefully around them, and traveled on. A little way further on, he met a young man, the handsomest person he had ever seen. His hair was very long, and he wore clothing made of strange skins. His moccasins were sewn with bright colored feathers. The young man said to him, "Did you see some weapons lying on the trail?"

"Yes," replied Scarface; "I saw them."

"But did you not touch them?" asked the young man.

"No; I thought some one had left them there, so I did not take them."

"You are not a thief," said the young man. "What is your name?"

"Scarface."

"Where are you going?"

"To the Sun."

"My name," said the young man, "is *A-pi-su'-ahts*. The Sun is my father; come, I will take you to our lodge. My father is not now at home, but he will come in at night."

Soon they came to the lodge. It was very large and handsome; strange medicine animals were painted on it. Behind, on a tripod, were strange weapons and beautiful clothes the Sun's. Scarface was ashamed to go in, but Morning Star said, "Do not be afraid, my friend; we are glad you have come."

They entered. One person was sitting there, *Ko-ko-mik'-e-is*, the Sun's wife, Morning Star's mother. She spoke to Scarface kindly, and gave him something to eat. "Why have you come so far from your people?" she asked.

Then Scarface told her about the beautiful girl he wanted to marry. "She belongs to the Sun," he said. "I have come to ask him for her."

When it was time for the Sun to come home, the Moon hid Scarface under a pile of robes. As soon as the Sun got to the doorway, he stopped, and said, "I smell a person."

"Yes, father," said Morning Star; "a good young man has come to see you. I know he is good, for he found some of my things on the trail and did not touch them."

Then Scarface came out from under the robes, and the Sun entered and sat down. "I am glad you have come to our lodge," he said. "Stay with us as long as you think best. My son is lonesome sometimes; be his friend."

The next day the Moon called Scarface out of the lodge, and said to him: "Go with Morning Star where you please, but never hunt near that big water; do not let him go there. It is the home of great birds which have long sharp bills; they kill people. I have had many sons, but these birds have killed them all. Morning Star is the only one left."

So Scarface stayed there a long time and hunted with Morning Star. One day they came near the water, and saw the big birds.

"Come," said Morning Star; "let us go and kill those birds."

"No, no!" replied Scarface; "we must not go there. Those are very terrible birds; they will kill us."

Morning Star would not listen. He ran towards the water, and
Scarface followed. He knew that he must kill the birds and save the
boy. If not, the Sun would be angry and might kill him. He ran
ahead and met the birds, which were coming towards him to fight,
and killed every one of them with his spear: not one was left. Then
the young men cut off their heads, and carried them home.
Morning Star's mother was glad when they told her what they had
done, and showed her the birds' heads. She cried, and called
Scarface "my son." When the Sun came home at night, she told
him about it, and he too was glad. "My son," he said to Scarface, "I
will not forget what you have this day done for me. Tell me now,
what can I do for you?"

"Hai'-yu" replied Scarface. "Hai'-yu, pity me. I am here to ask you
for that girl. I want to marry her. I asked her, and she was glad; but
she says you own her, that you told her not to marry."

"What you say is true," said the Sun. "I have watched the days, so I
know it. Now, then, I give her to you; she is yours. I am glad she
has been wise. I know she has never done wrong. The Sun pities
good women. They shall live a long time. So shall their husbands
and children. Now you will soon go home. Let me tell you
something. Be wise and listen: I am the only chief. Everything is
mine. I made the earth, the mountains, prairies, rivers, and forests.
I made the people and all the animals. This is why I say I alone am
the chief. I can never die. True, the winter makes me old and weak,
but every summer I grow young again."

Then said the Sun: "What one of all animals is smartest? The raven
is, for he always finds food. He is never hungry. Which one of all
the animals is most *Nat-o'-ye*? The buffalo is. Of all animals, I like
him best. He is for the people. He is your food and your shelter.
What part of his body is sacred? The tongue is. That is mine. What
else is sacred? Berries are. They are mine too. Come with me and
see the world." He took Scarface to the edge of the sky, and they
looked down and saw it. It is round and flat, and all around the

edge is the jumping-off place [or walls straight down]. Then said the Sun: "When any man is sick or in danger, his wife may promise to build me a lodge, if he recovers. If the woman is pure and true, then I will be pleased and help the man. But if she is bad, if she lies, then I will be angry. You shall build the lodge like the world, round, with walls, but first you must build a sweat house of a hundred sticks. It shall be like the sky [a hemisphere], and half of it shall be painted red. That is me. The other half you will paint black. That is the night."

Further said the Sun: "Which is the best, the heart or the brain? The brain is. The heart often lies, the brain never." Then he told Scarface everything about making the Medicine Lodge, and when he had finished, he rubbed a powerful medicine on his face, and the scar disappeared. Then he gave him two raven feathers, saying: "These are the sign for the girl, that I give her to you. They must always be worn by the husband of the woman who builds a Medicine Lodge."

The young man was now ready to return home. Morning Star and the Sun gave him many beautiful presents. The Moon cried and kissed him, and called him "my son." Then the Sun showed him the short trail. It was the Wolf Road (Milky Way). He followed it, and soon reached the ground.

It was a very hot day. All the lodge skins were raised, and the people sat in the shade. There was a chief, a very generous man, and all day long people kept coming to his lodge to feast and smoke with him. Early in the morning this chief saw a person sitting out on a butte near by, close wrapped in his robe. The chief's friends came and went, the sun reached the middle, and passed on, down towards the mountains. Still this person did not move. When it was almost night, the chief said: "Why does that person sit there so long? The heat has been strong, but he has never eaten nor drunk. He may be a stranger; go and ask him in."

So some young men went up to him, and said: "Why do you sit here in the great heat all day? Come to the shade of the lodges. The chief asks you to feast with him."

Then the person arose and threw off his robe, and they were surprised. He wore beautiful clothes. His bow, shield, and other weapons were of strange make. But they knew his face, although the scar was gone, and they ran ahead, shouting, "The scarface poor young man has come. He is poor no longer. The scar on his face is gone."

All the people rushed out to see him. "Where have you been?" they asked. "Where did you get all these pretty things?" He did not answer. There in the crowd stood that young woman; and taking the two raven feathers from his head, he gave them to her, and said: "The trail was very long, and I nearly died, but by those Helpers, I found his lodge. He is glad. He sends these feathers to you. They are the sign."

Great was her gladness then. They were married, and made the first Medicine Lodge, as the Sun had said. The Sun was glad. He gave them great age. They were never sick. When they were very old, one morning, their children said: "Awake! Rise and eat." They did not move. In the night, in sleep, without pain, their shadows had departed for the Sand Hills.

Inuit Story of the Northern Lights
(*An Eskimo Legend*)

Auroras - or Northern Lights - are believed to be the torches held in the hands of Spirits seeking the souls of those who have just died, to lead them over the abyss terminating the edge of the world. A narrow pathway leads across it to the land of brightness and plenty, where disease and pain are no more, and where food of all kinds is already in abundance. To this place none but the dead and the Raven can go. When the Spirits wish to communicate with the people of the Earth, they make a whistling noise, and the Earth people answer only in a whispering tone. The Eskimo say that they are able to call the Aurora and converse with it. They send messages to the dead through these Spirits.

It is the general belief of the Indians that after a man dies his spirit is somewhere on the earth or in the sky, we do not know exactly where, but we are sure that his spirit still lives. . . . So it is with Wakantanka. We believe that he is everywhere, yet he is to us as the spirits of our friends, whose voices we can not hear.

Chased-by-Bears, Santee-Yanktonai Sioux

How Old Man Above Created the World
(*A Shasta Legend*)

Long, long ago, when the world was so new that even the stars were dark, it was very, very flat. Chareya, Old Man Above, could not see through the dark to the new, flat Earth. Neither could he step down to it because it was so far below him. With a large stone he bored a hole in the sky. Then through the hole he pushed down masses of ice and snow, until a great pyramid rose from the plain. Old Man Above climbed down through the hole he had made in the sky, stepping from cloud to cloud, until he could put his foot on top the mass of ice and snow. Then with one long step he reached the Earth.

The sun shone through the hole in the sky and began to melt the ice and snow. It made holes in the ice and snow. When it was soft, Chareya bored with his finger into the earth, here and there, and planted the first trees. Streams from the melting snow watered the new trees and made them grow. Then he gathered the leaves which fell from the trees and blew upon them. They became birds. He took a stick and broke it into pieces. Out of the small end he made fishes and placed them in the mountain streams. Of the middle of the stick, he made all the animals except the grizzly bear. From the big end of the stick came the grizzly bear, who was made master of all. Grizzly was large and strong and cunning. When the Earth was new he walked upon two feet and carried a large club. So strong was Grizzly that Old Man Above feared the creature he had made.

Therefore, so that he might be safe, Chareya hollowed out the pyramid of ice and snow as a teepee. There he lived for thousands of snows. The Indians knew he lived there because they could see the smoke curling from the smoke hole of his teepee. When the pale-face came, Old Man Above went away. There is no longer any smoke from the smoke hole. White men call the teepee Mount Shasta.

A warrior who had more than he needed would make a feast. He went around and invited the old and needy. . . The man who could thank the food—some worthy old medicine man or warrior—said, ". . . . look to the old, they are worthy of old age; they have seen their days and proven themselves. With the help of the Great Spirit, they have attained a ripe old age. At this age the old can predict or give knowledge or wisdom, whatever it is; it is so. At the end is a cane. You and your family shall get to where the cane is."

Black Elk, Oglala Sioux holy man

Legend of Wolf Boy
(A Kiowa Legend)

There was a camp of Kiowa. There were a young man, his wife, and his brother. They set out by themselves to look for game. This young man would leave his younger brother and his wife in camp and go out to look for game. Every time his brother would leave, the boy would go to a high hill nearby and sit there all day until his brother returned. One time before the boy went as usual to the hill, his sister-in-law said, "Why are you so lonesome?" Let us be sweethearts. "The boy answered, "No, I love my brother and I would not want to do that." She said, "Your brother would not know. Only you and I would know. He would not find out." "No, I think a great deal of my brother. I would not want to do that."

One night as they all went to sleep the young woman went to where the boy used to sit on the hill. She began to dig. She dug a hole deep enough so that no one would ever hear him. She covered it by placing a hide over the hole, and she made it look so natural so nobody would notice it. She went back to the camp and laid down. Next day the older brother went hunting and the younger brother went to where he used to sit. The young woman watched him and saw him drop out of sight. She went up the hill and looked into the pit and said, "I guess you want to make love now. If you are willing to be my sweetheart I will let you out. If not, you will have to stay in there until you die." The boy said, "I will not." After the young man returned home, he asked his wife where his little brother was. She said, "I have not seen him since you left, but he went up on the hill."

That night as they went to bed the young man said to his wife that he thought he heard a voice somewhere. She said, " It is only the Wolves that you hear." The young man did not sleep all night. He said to his wife, "You must have scolded him to make him go; he may have gone back home." I did not say anything to him. Every day when you go hunting he goes to that hill." Next day they broke camp and went back to the main camp to see if he was there. He was not there. They concluded that he had died. His father and mother cried over him.

The boy staying in the pit was crying; he was starving. He looked up and saw something. A Wolf was pulling off the old hide. The Wolf said, "Why are you down there?" The boy told him what happened, that the woman caused him to be in there. The Wolf said, "I will get you out. If I get you out, you will be my son." He heard the Wolf howling. When he looked up again, there was a pack of Wolves. They started to dig in the side of the pit until they reached him and he could crawl out. It was very cold. As night came on, the Wolves lay all around him and on top of him to keep him warm.

Next morning the Wolves asked what he ate. He said that he ate meat. So the Wolves went out and found Buffalo and killed a calf and brought it to him. The boy had nothing to butcher it with, so the Wolf tore the calf to pieces for the boy to get out what he wanted. The boy ate till he was full. The Wolf who got him out asked the others if they knew where there was a flint knife. One said that he had seen one somewhere. He told him to get it. After that, when the Wolves killed for him he would butcher it himself.

Some time after that, a man from the camp was out hunting, and he observed a pack of Wolves and among them a man. He rode up to see if he could recognize this man. He got near enough only to see that it was a man. He returned to camp and told the people he had seen a man with some Wolves. They considered that it might be the young man who had been lost some time before. The camp had killed off all the Buffalo. Some young men after butchering had left to kill Wolves (as they did after killing Buffalo). They noticed a young man with a pack of Wolves. The Wolves saw the men, and they ran off. The young man ran off with them.

Next day the whole camp went out to see who the young man was. The saw the Wolves and the young man with them. They pursued the young man. They overtook him and caught him. He bit them like a Wolf. After they caught him, they heard the Wolves howling in the distance. The young man told his father and brother to free him so he could hear what the Wolves were saying. They said if they loosened him, he would not come back. However they loosened him and he went out and met the Wolves. Then he returned to camp.

"How did you come to be among them?" asked the father and brother. He told how his sister-in-law had dug the hole, and he fell in, and the Wolves had gotten him out, and he had lived with them ever since.

The Wolf had aid to him that someone must come in his place, that they were to wind Buffalo gut around the young woman and send her. The young woman's father and mother found out what she had done to the boy. They said to her husband that she had done wrong and for him to do as the Wolf had directed and take her to him and let him eat her up. So the husband of the young woman took her and wound the guts around her and led her to where the Wolf had directed. The whole camp went to see, and the Wolf Boy said, "Let me take her to my father Wolf." Then he took her and stopped at a distance and howled like a Wolf, and they saw the Wolves coming from everywhere. He said to his Wolf father, "Here is the one you were to have in my place." The Wolves came and tore her up.

The Bird that Turned the Meat Bitter
(A Mandan Legend)

Looking about the lodges in the village, Coyote saw strings of jerked meat, but the people were lean. He asked why this was. The people said, "When we go hunting, only the fastest butchers can get their meat home in good condition. There is a Raven which flies over calling "Get bitter! Get bitter!" (gi-ba in Mandan) and the meat turns bitter." Coyote asked for a sample. He chewed but could not swallow the meat, it was so bitter. He said, "I must have this thing righted." He sent the young girl after firewood and had it piled ready to light, first laying down manure because it keeps the flame a long time. Then he had the men get timber rope and make a snare. He filled up his pipe and asked help of his fellow creatures. The big Spider came to his aid, and he lighted the pipe for the Spider to smoke. Now the Raven lived in a hollow tree out of which it flew when the men were butchering. Big Spider said, "It is easy to snare that bird. Be ready to snare him into the fire and let him burn. Some of his feathers will fly into the air and turn into birds. When you see a white Raven fly out a cry 'At the end of the world there shall be seen a white Raven as a sign that the world is coming to an end' that will be the last of it."

They sent out young men into the hills scouting. These reported Buffalo. They made ready for the hunt. The fastest runners went ahead to encircle the herd. Buffalo always run towards the wind, but the runners drove them towards the other hunters. These formed a corral where they slaughtered the whole herd. The men with large families packed meat home; others followed behind. Meanwhile, some watched by the hollow tree. When the bird came out, before it could cry, Coyote caught it by the neck and pulled it to the ground. It had the head of a man and the body of a bird. The face was human but had no hair. The body had wings and a long neck. It was a frightful thing to see. Coyote clubbed the bird and threw it into the flames. Feathers flew up and turned into birds and flew away. The unburned bones Coyote crushed with his club. Finally out flew a white Raven and said, "When the world is about to end I will come to you again!" So Coyote told the people that was to be a sign to them.

Blue Jay's Skinny Legs
(*A Flathead Legend*)

It happened a long time ago, before the arrival of the White brothers / sisters. There was a chief who had a very beautiful daughter. He wanted to make sure that she married a strong and healthy man. As the young men began to come around to flirt with his daughter, he became worried. He decided to reduce the odds by having a race. He informed all the young men that the one with the strongest legs could marry his daughter.

Coyote was crafty and a good runner with a lot of power, so he came first. He showed how long his legs were and how fast he could run. Then Deer came, a very handsome and strong buck. He showed how powerful his legs were at jumping, although they were somewhat knotted up. Then Grizzly Bear came along. Bear stood up and growled so everyone could see that he had very powerful and strong legs. So he claimed the girl.

But Blue Jay hollered that it was not fair, that others should still be considered. While the others were showing their legs, he hid behind an old log, where he had gathered a lot of tree moss and used clay to pack it around his legs. They looked larger and stronger than anyone's , even bigger than Grizzly Bears. But to sweeten the pot, Blue Jay also offered all kinds of beautiful feathers he had obtained from all of his different bird relations. The old chief was fooled by this and let his daughter go with him Blue Jay had to carry his new wife across the stream in order to reach his tepee on the other side. As he began the hard journey, The water softened the moss and clay, so they fell from his legs.

When he climbed up on the other side of the stream bank, everyone began to laugh. Grizzly Bear came down and claimed his prize, and with his strong legs carried his new wife up the side of the mountain. Anytime he tries to come back and visit , the Blue Jay will start squawking all over the forest, and he makes a terrible noise. He does this because he is jealous and doesn't like to be laughed at.

Here is the same story, told slightly differently.

The chief had a daughter who was old enough to marry. He informed the young men that one with the strongest legs could have her. Coyote showed how long and fast he could run and claimed the girl. Bear flexed his leg muscles to show how big and strong they were, and he claimed the girl. Jay sneaked off into the woods where he gathered some black moss that hangs from trees. He wrapped the moss around his legs to make them look large. The chief was fooled by his trick and proclaimed him the winner. Jay had to carry his new wife across a stream in order to reach hiss teepee, and the water softened the moss so it fell off his legs. When he climbed the bank on the opposite side of the stream, everyone saw his little skinny legs and they all laughed.

The Wolf
(Cherokee)

Feared and hated by men the world over, the mighty wolf has been plagued by all forms of evil stories, myths and legends. Hunted, trapped and killed to the point of extinction, many of these majestic animals are gone forever -- their breeds and blood lines never to be seen again.

In spite of the many horror stories of wolves hunting, tracking and killing humans, no such event has ever been confirmed. Their eerie and lonely howl, which can make the blood run cold, is merely their form of communication. Each howl, with its tone, depth, length and frequency carries a different message to the pack, or to the partner who is out of sight. They're merely "talking".

If you carry wolf medicine, here are some characteristics that sound familiar to you:

You are fiercely loyal -- to friends, family, ideals and principles. There is no compromise for you.

You are very territorial. You protect all that is yours and your family's at any expense. You are fearless in your protection, but not reckless. You plan your strategy carefully, and wait for the opportune moment for most powerful effect.

You have a strong family structure. There is no doubt who the elders, patriarchs and parents are, or about their roles in the family structure. Disobedience, selfishness and unruly behavior is not tolerated as there are strong boundaries for the young. They are taught well and carefully so that they may assume leadership roles in their own family structures.

You have an unrelenting sense of adventure. You love to explore new things, to stretch out for new horizons. You have a thirst for knowledge and for learning new things. You are eager to share these things, which makes you a natural teacher. Your adventures may take you away from home and family, but it is important that you have this base of security to return to.

You have an unrelenting need to be alone. You are so busy being the protector, the provider, the teacher, and the trailblazer, that it's very easy for you to become exhausted and burned out. In order to re-charge your spirit, and keep your balance, it is critical that you have time to be alone with your thoughts and your own sense of self. This is one side of your nature that must not be overlooked. Even if you lock yourself in the bathroom for 15 minutes a day, the time alone must be honored if you are to have value to those you care for.

Wolf is power. Wolf is honor. Wolf is integrity. Brother Wolf; Sister Wolf -- I honor you

The Legend of the Cherokee Rose
(Cherokee Legend)

In the latter half of 1838, Cherokee People who had not voluntarily moved west earlier were forced to leave their homes in the East.

The trail to the West was long and treacherous and many were dying along the way. The People's hearts were heavy with sadness and their tears mingled with the dust of the trail.

The Elders knew that the survival of the children depended upon the strength of the women. One evening around the campfire, the Elders called upon Heaven Dweller, *ga lv la di e hi*. They told Him of the People's suffering and tears. They were afraid the children would not survive to rebuild the Cherokee Nation.

Gal v la di e hi spoke to them, "To let you know how much I care, I will give you a sign. In the morning, tell the women to look back along the trail. Where their tears have fallen, I will cause to grow a plant that will have seven leaves for the seven clans of the Cherokee. Amidst the plant will be a delicate white rose with five petals. In the center of the blossom will be a pile of gold to remind the Cherokee of the white man's greed for the gold found on the Cherokee homeland. This plant will be sturdy and strong with stickers on all the stems. It will defy anything which tries to destroy it."

The next morning the Elders told the women to look back down the trail. A plant was growing fast and covering the trail where they had walked. As the women watched, blossoms formed and slowly opened. They forgot their sadness. Like the plant the women began to feel strong and beautiful. As the plant protected its blossoms, they knew they would have the courage and determination to protect their children who would begin a new Nation in the West.

Sunset. Then I was standing on the highest mountain of them all, and round about beneath me was the whole hoop of the world. And while I stood there I saw more than I can tell and I understood more than I saw; for I was seeing in a sacred manner the shapes of all things in the spirit, and the shape of all shapes as they must live together like one being.

And I say the sacred hoop of my people was one of the many hoops that made one circle, wide as daylight and as starlight, and in the center grew one mighty flowering tree to shelter all the children of one mother and one father. And I saw that it was holy...

But anywhere is the center of the world.
- *Black Elk 3*

Contents of the Medicine Bag

The contents of each Medicine Bag represent specific totems for specific birth times from around the Medicine Wheel:

The Spirit Rocks and/or animal fetishes represent your own animal totem and your Clan totem

The mineral stone represents your mineral totem

The cloth-wrapped bundle contains your plant totem in seed or herb form

The glass, wooden or stone bead represents your color totem, as does the cloth and ribbon with which your plant totem is wrapped

The empty cloth bundle is to hold some soil from your own most favorite spot on earth

Native Americans, who called themselves "the People," always carried a Medicine Bag or Pouch. Medicine Bags had special power and were good medicine; they were considered sacred. They provided protection, and helped connect with Spirit. The contents of the Medicine Bag were intensely personal, and might include a rock from a sacred place, a special animal tooth, a certain herb, a feather, an animal fetish.

Raven's Medicine

Those who carry Raven Medicine also carry a heavy responsibility to Spirit. Raven is the messenger of magic from the great void where all knowledge waits for us. He is also the symbol of changes in consciousness, of levels of awareness and of perception. He carries the mark of the shape-shifter. He is the carrier of healing energy from distances.

Those of you who have asked for messages of light and healing and prayer on this list have asked for raven medicine.

What all of this means to us in the modern-day world is that raven medicine gives you the ability to get inside another's head and heart, and to understand them from the inside out, so to speak. You can "become" that other person because of the depth of your understanding of them, and it is not necessary to be in their physical presence for that to happen.

Spiritual healers and counselors who are skilled in their abilities are using raven power for they have a depth of understanding and empathy not shared by all. Because of this power, they have the ability to actually alter another's perception and behavior. They are able to work real magic in bringing peace, healing and understanding to others.

Here is the heavy responsibility, and the dangers, in raven medicine. As with all things, these powers can be used for dark purposes. It enables the carrier to manipulate and coerce others into doing their will to the detriment of the other.

This medicine can be used for selfish and self-serving purposes for the ego and greed of the carrier. Because of the power of the levels in understanding others, a practitioner of the black arts can use raven for destructive purposes.

If you carry raven medicine, you must always use it in the light for the highest and best interests of others. You must use it for the good and well being of others, and never for your own selfish motives even though you may be tempted when times are bad. Raven medicine demands that you walk in the light in all things. That's heavy with responsibility for your own thoughts and deeds.

Work your magic in the light -- you are Raven.

The Legend of the Dream Catcher

The Old Ones tell that dreams hold great power and drift about at night before coming to the sleeping ones.

To keep the dreamer safe, the Old Ones created a special web, the Dream Catcher, to hang above their sleeping places. When dreams traveled the web paths, the bad dreams lost their way and became entangled, disappearing with the first rays of daybreak, like the morning dew on the grass. The good dreams, knowing their way, passed through the center and were guided gently to the sleeping ones.

An old Sioux Indian legend says that dream catchers were hung in lodges and teepees to ensure peaceful dreams. The good dreams, knowing the way, slip through the webbing and slide down the soft feather to the sleeper. The bad dreams, not knowing the way, become entangled in the web, and melt at the first light of the new day. Small dream catchers were hung on cradleboards, so that infants would have only good dreams.

Dreams are not just for the young. They are for children of all ages. To dream is to live, without our dreams we will cease to live and merely exist. Dare to dream and live!

Unknown

The First Fire

In the beginning there was no fire and the world was cold. Then the Thunders (Ani'-Hyun'tikwsla'ski) who lived up in Galun'lati, sent their lightning and put fire into the bottom of a hollow sycamore tree which grew on an island.

The animals knew it was there, because they could see the smoke, but they could not get to it because of the water. They held a council to see what to do, and every animal that could fly or swim was anxious to go after the fire. The Raven, large and strong was sent first. He flew to the sycamore, but while he was wondering what to do next, the fire scorched all his feathers black and he came back without the fire. Next, the little Screech-owl (Wa'huhu') volunteered to go, but once in the island, a blast of hot air came up and nearly burned out his eyes. He managed to fly back home, but his eyes are red to this day. Then the Hooting Owl (U'guku') and the Horned Owl (Tskili') went, but by the time they arrived, the fire was burning so fiercely that the smoke nearly blinded them, and the ashes carried up by the wind made white rings about their eyes and they were never able to get rid of them.

Now no more birds would venture, and so the little Uksu'hi snake, the black racer, said he would swim to the island and bring the fire back. He swam across to the island and crawled through the grass to the tree, and went in by a small hole at the bottom. The heat and smoke were too much for him, and after dodging about blindly over the hot ashes until he was almost on fire himself, he managed to get out, but his body had been scorched black, and he has ever since had the habit of darting and doubling on his track as if trying to escape from close quarters. He came back, and the great blacksnake, Gulegi, "The Climber", offered to go. He swam over to the island and climbed up tree on the outside, but when he put his head down into the hole, the smoke choked him so that fell into the burning stump and before he could climb out again he too was as black as the Uksu'hi.

Now they held another council, but all the animals had an excuse for not going because they were all afraid until at last Kanane'ski Amai'yehi (the Water Spider) said she would go. This is the water spider with black downy hair and red stripes on her body. She can run on top of the water or dive to the bottom, so there would be no trouble reaching the island, but the question was, How could she bring back the fire? "I'll manage that" said the Water Spider. So she spun a thread from her body and wove it into a tusti bowl, which she fastened on her back. Then she crossed over to the island and through the grass to where the fire was still burning. She placed one little coal of fire into her bowl, and came back with it. Ever since we have had fire, and the Water Spider still keeps her tusti bowl.

Old-Man Remakes the World
(Chippewa)

The sun was just sinking behind the hills when we started for War Eagle's lodge.

"To-morrow will be a fine day," said Other-person, "for grandfather says that a red sky is always the sun's promise of fine weather, and the sun cannot lie."

"Yes," said Bluebird, "and he said that when this moon was new it travelled well south for this time of year and its points were up. That means fine, warm weather."

"I wish I knew as much as grandfather," said Fine-bow with pride.

The pipe was laid aside at once upon our entering the lodge and the old warrior said:

"I have told you that Old-man taught the animals and the birds all they know. He made them and therefore knew just what each would have to understand in order to make his living. They have never forgotten anything he told them -- even to this day. Their grandfathers told the young ones what they had been told, just as I am telling you the things you should know. Be like the birds and animals -- tell your children and grandchildren what I have told you, that our people may always know how things were made, and why strange things are true.

"Yes -- Old-man taught the Beaver how to build his dams to make the water deeper; taught the Squirrel to plant the pine-nut so that another tree might grow and have nuts for his children; told the Bear to go to sleep in the winter, when the snow made hard travelling for his short legs -- told him to sleep, and promised him that he would need no meat while he slept. All winter long the Bear sleeps and eats nothing, because Old-man told him that he could. He sleeps so much in the winter that he spends most of his time in summer hunting.

"It was Old-man who showed the Owl how to hunt at night and it was Old-man that taught the Weasel all his wonderful ways -- his bloodthirsty ways -- for the Weasel is the bravest of the animal-people, considering his size. He taught the Beaver one strange thing that you have noticed, and that is to lay sticks on the creek-bottoms, so that they will stay there as long as he wants them to.

"Whenever the animal-people got into trouble they always sought Old-man and told him about it. All were busy working and making a living, when one day it commenced to rain. That was nothing, of course, but it didn't stop as it had always done before. No, it kept right on raining until the rivers overran their banks, and the water chased the Weasel out of his hole in the ground. Yes, and it found the Rabbit's hiding-place and made him leave it. It crept into the lodge of the Wolf at night and frightened his wife and children. It poured into the den of the Bear among the rocks and he had to move. It crawled under the logs in the forest and found the Mice-people. Out it went to the plains and chased them out of their homes in the buffalo skulls. At last the Beavers' dams broke under the strain and that made everything worse. It was bad -- very bad, indeed. Everybody except the fish-people were frightened and all went to find Old-man that they might tell him what had happened. Finally they found his fire, far up on a timbered bench, and they said that they wanted a council right away.

"It was a strange sight to see the Eagle sitting next to the Grouse; the Rabbit sitting close to the Lynx; the Mouse right under the very nose of the Bobcat, and the tiny Humming-bird talking to the Hawk in a whisper, as though they had always been great friends. All about Old-man's fire they sat and whispered or talked in signs. Even the Deer spoke to the Mountain-lion, and the Antelope told the Wolf that he was glad to see him, because fear had made them all friends.

"The whispering and the sign-making stopped when Old-man raised his hand-like that" (here War Eagle raised his hand with the palm outward) -- "and asked them what was troubling them.

"The Bear spoke first, of course, and told how the water had made him move his camp. He said all the animal-people were moving their homes, and he was afraid they would be unable to find good camping-places, because of the water. Then the Beaver spoke, because he is wise and all the forest-people know it. He said his dams would not hold back the water that came against them; that the whole world was a lake, and that he thought they were on an island. He said he could live in the water longer than most people, but that as far as he could see they would all die except, perhaps, the fish-people, who stayed in the water all the time, anyhow. He said he couldn't think of a thing to do -- then he sat down and the sign-talking and whispering commenced again.

"Old-man smoked a long time -- smoked and thought hard. Finally he grabbed his magic stone axe, and began to sing his war song. Then the rest knew he had made up his mind and knew what he would do. Swow! he struck a mighty pine-tree a blow, and it fell down. Swow! down went another and another, until he had ten times ten of the longest, straightest, and largest trees in all the world lying side by side before him. Then Old-man chopped off the limbs, and with the aid of magic rolled the great logs tight together. With withes of willow that he told the Beaver to cut for him, he bound the logs fast together until they were all as one. It was a monstrous raft that Old-man had built, as he sang his song in the darkness. At last he cried, 'Ho! everybody hurry and sit on this raft I have made'; and they did hurry.

"It was not long till the water had reached the logs; then it crept in between them, and finally it went on past the raft and off into the forest, looking for more trouble.

"By and by the raft began to groan, and the willow withes squeaked and cried out as though ghost-people were crying in the night. That was when the great logs began to tremble as the water lifted them from the ground. Rain was falling -- night was there, and fear made cowards of the bravest on the raft. All through the forest there were bad noises -- noises that make the heart cold -- as the raft bumped against great trees rising from the earth that they were leaving forever.

"Higher and higher went the raft; higher than the bushes; higher than the limbs on the trees; higher than the Woodpecker's nest; higher than the tree tops, and even higher than the mountains. Then the world was no more, for the water had whipped the land in the war it made against it.

"Day came, and still the rain was falling. Night returned, and yet the rain came down. For many days and nights they drifted in the falling rain; whirling and twisting about while the water played with the great raft, as a Bear would play with a Mouse. It was bad, and they were all afraid -- even Old-man himself was scared.

"At last the sun came but there was no land. All was water. The water was the world. It reached even to the sky and touched it all about the edges. All were hungry, and some of them were grumbling, too. There are always grumblers when there is great trouble, but they are not the ones who become great chiefs -- ever.

"Old-man sat in the middle of the raft and thought. He knew that something must be done, but he didn't know what. Finally he said: 'Ho! Chipmunk, bring me the Spotted Loon. Tell him I want him.'

"The Chipmunk found the Spotted Loon and told him that Old-man wanted him, so the Loon went to where Old-man sat. When he got there, Old-man said:

"'Spotted Loon you are a great diver. Nobody can dive as you can. I made you that way and I know. If you will dive and swim down to the world I think you might bring me some of the dirt that it is made of -- then I am sure I can make another world.'

"'It is too deep, this water,' replied the Loon, 'I am afraid I shall drown.'

"'Well, what if you do?' said Old-man. 'I gave you life, and if you lose it this way I will return it to you. You shall live again!'

"'All right, Old-man,' he answered, 'I am willing to try'; so he waddled to the edge of the raft. He is a poor walker -- the Loon, and you know I told you why. It was all because Old-man kicked him in the back the night he painted all the Duck-people.

"Down went the Spotted Loon, and long he stayed beneath the water. All waited and watched, and longed for good luck, but when he came to the top he was dead. Everybody groaned -- all felt badly, I can tell you, as Old-man laid the dead Loon on the logs. The Loon's wife was crying, but Old-man told her to shut up and she did.

"Then Old-man blew his own breath into the Loon's bill, and he came back to life.

"'What did you see, Brother Loon?' asked Old-man, while everybody crowded as close as he could.

"'Nothing but water,' answered the Loon, 'we shall all die here, I cannot reach the world by swimming. My heart stops working.'

"There were many brave ones on the raft, and the Otter tried to reach the world by diving; and the Beaver, and the Gray Goose, and the Gray Goose's wife; but all died in trying, and all were given a new life by Old-man. Things were bad and getting worse. Everybody was cross, and all wondered what Old-man would do next, when somebody laughed.

"All turned to see what there could be to laugh at, at such a time, and Old-man turned about just in time to see the Muskrat bid good-by to his wife -- that was what they were laughing at. But he paid no attention to Old-man or the rest, and slipped from the raft to the water. Flip! -- his tail cut the water like a knife, and he was gone. Some laughed again, but all wondered at his daring, and waited with little hope in their hearts; for the Muskrat wasn't very great, they thought.

"He was gone longer than the Loon, longer than the Beaver, longer than the Otter or the Gray Goose or his wife, but when he came to the surface of the water he was dead.

"Old-man brought Muskrat back to life, and asked him what he had seen on his journey. Muskrat said: 'I saw trees, Old-man, but I died before I got to them.'

"Old-man told him he was brave. He said his people should forever be great if he succeeded in bringing some dirt to the raft; so just as soon as the Muskrat was rested he dove again.

"When he came up he was dead, but clinched in his tiny hand Old-man found some dirt -- not much, but a little. A second time Old-man gave the Muskrat his breath, and told him that he must go once more, and bring dirt. He said there was not quite enough in the first lot, so after resting a while the Muskrat tried a third time and a third time he died, but brought up a little more dirt.

"Everybody on the raft was anxious now, and they were all crowding about Old-man; but he told them to stand back, and they did. Then he blew his breath in Muskrat's mouth a third time, and a third time he lived and joined his wife.

"Old-man then dried the dirt in his hands, rubbing it slowly and singing a queer song. Finally it was dry; then he settled the hand that held the dirt in the water slowly, until the water touched the dirt. The dry dirt began to whirl about and then Old-man blew upon it. Hard he blew and waved his hands, and the dirt began to grow in size right before their eyes. Old-man kept blowing and waving his hands until the dirt became real land, and the trees began to grow. So large it grew that none could see across it. Then he stopped his blowing and sang some more. Everybody wanted to get off the raft, but Old-man said 'no.'

"'Come here, Wolf,' he said, and the Wolf came to him.

"'You are swift of foot and brave. Run around this land I have made, that I may know how large it is.'

"The Wolf started, and it took him half a year to get back to the raft. He was very poor from much running, too, but Old-man said the world wasn't big enough yet so he blew some more, and again sent the Wolf out to run around the land. He never came back -- no, the Old-man had made it so big that the Wolf died of old age before he got back to the raft. Then all the people went out upon the land to make their living, and they were happy, there, too.

"After they had been on the land for a long time Old-man said: 'Now I shall make a man and a woman, for I am lonesome living with you people. He took two or three handfuls of mud from the world he had made, and molded both a man and a woman. Then he set them side by side and breathed upon them. They lived! -- and he made them very strong and healthy -- very beautiful to look upon. Chippewas, he called these people, and they lived happily on that world until a white man saw an Eagle sailing over the land and came to look about. He stole the woman -- that white man did; and that is where all the tribes came from that we know to-day. None are pure of blood but the two humans he made of clay, and their own children. And they are the Chippewas!

"That is a long story and now you must hurry to bed. To-morrow night I will tell you another story -- Ho!"

Grown men can learn from very little children
for the hearts of the little children are pure.
Therefore, the Great Spirit may show to them
many things which older people miss.

Black Elk

How the World was Made
(Cherokee)

The earth is a great island floating in a sea of water, and suspended at each of the four cardinal points by a cord hanging down from the sky vault, which is of solid rock. When the world grows old and worn out, the people will die and the cords will break and let the earth sink down into the ocean, and all will be water again. The Indians are afraid of this.

When all was water, the animals were above in Gälûñ'lätï, beyond the arch; but it was very much crowded, and they were wanting more room. They wondered what was below the water, and at last Dâyuni'sï, "Beaver's Grandchild," the little Water-beetle, offered to go and see if it could learn. It darted in every direction over the surface of the water, but could find no firm place to rest. Then it dived to the bottom and came up with some soft mud, which began to grow and spread on every side until it became the island which we call the earth. It was afterward fastened to the sky with four cords, but no one remembers who did this.

At first the earth was flat and very soft and wet. The animals were anxious to get down, and sent out different birds to see if it was yet dry, but they found no place to alight and came back again to Gälûñ'lätï. At last it seemed to be time, and they sent out the Buzzard and told him to go and make ready for them. This was the Great Buzzard, the father of all the buzzards we see now. He flew all over the earth, low down near the ground, and it was still soft. When he reached the Cherokee country, he was very tired, and his wings began to flap and strike the ground, and wherever they struck the earth there was a valley, and where they turned up again there was a mountain. When the animals above saw this, they were afraid that the whole world would be mountains, so they called him back, but the Cherokee country remains full of mountains to this day.

When the earth was dry and the animals came down, it was still dark, so they got the sun and set it in a track to go every day across the island from east to west, just overhead. It was too hot this way, and Tsiska'gïlï', the Red Crawfish, had his shell scorched a bright red, so that his meat was spoiled; and the Cherokee do not eat it. The conjurers put the sun another hand-breadth higher in the air, but it was still too hot. They raised it another time, and another, until it was seven handbreadths high and just under the sky arch. Then it was right, and they left it so. This is why the conjurers call the highest place Gûlkwâ'gine Di'gälûñ'lätiyûñ', "the seventh height," because it is seven hand-breadths above the earth. Every day the sun goes along under this arch, and returns at night on the upper side to the starting place.

There is another world under this, and it is like ours in everything-- animals, plants, and people--save that the seasons are different. The streams that come down from the mountains are the trails by which we reach this underworld, and the springs at their heads are the doorways by which we enter, it, but to do this one must fast and, go to water and have one of the underground people for a guide. We know that the seasons in the underworld are different from ours, because the water in the springs is always warmer in winter and cooler in summer than the outer air.

When the animals and plants were first made--we do not know by whom--they were told to watch and keep awake for seven nights, just as young men now fast and keep awake when they pray to their medicine. They tried to do this, and nearly all were awake through the first night, but the next night several dropped off to sleep, and the third night others were asleep, and then others, until, on the seventh night, of all the animals only the owl, the panther, and one or two more were still awake. To these were given the power to see and to go about in the dark, and to make prey of the birds and animals which must sleep at night. Of the trees only the cedar, the pine, the spruce, the holly, and the laurel were awake to the end, and to them it was given to be always green and to be greatest for medicine, but to the others it was said: "Because you have not endured to the end you shall lose your, hair every winter."

Men came after the animals and plants. At first there were only a brother and sister until he struck her with a fish and told her to multiply, and so it was. In seven days a child was born to her, and thereafter every seven days another, and they increased very fast until there was danger that the world could not keep them. Then it was made that a woman should have only one child in a year, and it has been so ever since.

When the white man discovered this
country Indians were running it.
No taxes - no debt, women did all the work
White man thought he could improve on a system like this.

Old Cherokee Saying

Origin of Disease and Medicine

In the old days the beasts, birds, fishes, insects, and plants could all talk, and they and the people lived together in peace and friendship. But as time went on the people increased so rapidly that their settlements spread over the whole earth, and the poor animals found themselves beginning to be cramped for room. This was bad enough, but to make it worse Man invented bows, knives, blowguns, spears, and hooks, and began to slaughter the larger animals, birds, and fishes for their flesh or their skins, while the smaller creatures, such as the frogs and worms, were crushed and trodden upon without thought, out of pure carelessness or contempt. So the animals resolved to consult upon measures for their common safety.

The Bears were the first to meet in council in their townhouse under Kuwâ'hï mountain, the "Mulberry place," and the old White Bear chief presided. After each in turn had complained of the way in which Man killed their friends, ate their flesh, and used their skins for his own purposes, it was decided to begin war at once against him. Some one asked what weapons Man used to destroy them. "Bows and arrows, of course, cried all the Bears in chorus. "And what are they made of?" was the next question. "The bow of wood, and the string of our entrails," replied one of the Bears. It was then proposed that they make a bow and some arrows and see if they, could not use the same weapons against Man himself. So one Bear got a nice piece of locust wood and another sacrificed himself for the good of the rest in order to furnish a piece of his entrails for the string. But when everything was ready and the first Bear stepped up to make the trial, it was found that in letting the arrow fly after drawing back the bow, his long claws caught the string and spoiled the shot. This was annoying, but some one suggested that they might trim his claws, which was accordingly done, and on a second trial it was found that the arrow went straight to the mark. But here the chief, the old White Bear, objected, saying it was necessary that they should have long claws in order to be able to climb trees. "One of us has already died to furnish the bowstring, and if we now cut off our claws we must all starve together. It is better to trust to the teeth and claws that nature gave us, for it is plain that man's weapons were not intended for us."

No one could think of any better plan, so the old chief dismissed the council and the Bears dispersed to the woods and thickets without having concerted any way to prevent the increase of the human race. Had the result of the council been otherwise, we should now be at war with the Bears, but as it is, the hunter does not even ask the Bear's pardon when he kills one.

The Deer next held a council under their chief, the Little Deer, and after some talk decided to send rheumatism to every hunter who should kill one of them unless he took care to ask their pardon for the offense. They sent notice of their decision to the nearest settlement of Indians and told them at the same time what to do when necessity forced them to kill one of the Deer tribe. Now, whenever the hunter shoots a Deer, the Little Deer, who is swift as the wind and can not be wounded, runs quickly up to the spot and, bending over the blood-stains, asks the spirit of the Deer if it has heard the prayer of the hunter for pardon. If the reply be "Yes," all is well, and the Little Deer goes on his way; but if the reply be "No," he follows on the trail of the hunter, guided by the drops of blood on the ground, until he arrives at his cabin in the settlement, when the Little Deer enters invisibly and strikes the hunter with rheumatism, so that he becomes at once a helpless cripple. No hunter who has regard for his health ever fails to ask pardon of the Deer for killing it, although some hunters who have not learned the prayer may try to turn aside the Little Deer from his pursuit by building a fire behind them in the trail.

Next came the Fishes and Reptiles, who had their own complaints against Man. They held their council together and determined to make their victims dream of snakes twining about them in slimy folds and blowing foul breath in their faces, or to make them dream of eating raw or decaying fish, so that they would lose appetite, sicken, and die. This is why people dream about snakes and fish.

Finally the Birds, Insects, and smaller animals came together for the same purpose, and the Grubworm was chief of the council. It was decided that each in turn should give an opinion, and then they would vote on the question as to whether or not Man was guilty. Seven votes should be enough to condemn him. One after another denounced Man's cruelty and injustice toward the other animals and voted in favor of his death. The Frog spoke first, saying: "We must do something to check the increase of the race, or people will become so numerous that we shall be crowded from off the earth. See how they have kicked me about because I'm ugly, as they say, until my back is covered with sores;" and here he showed the spots on his skin. Next came the Bird--no one remembers now which one it was--who condemned Man "because he burns my feet off," meaning the way in which the hunter barbecues birds by impaling them on a stick set over the fire, so that their feathers and tender feet are singed off. Others followed in the same strain. The Ground-squirrel alone ventured to say a good word for Man, who seldom hurt him because he was so small, but this made the others so angry that they fell upon the Ground-squirrel and tore him with their claws, and the stripes are on his back to this day.

They began then to devise and name so many new diseases, one after another, that had not their invention at last failed them, no one of the human race would have been able to survive. The Grubworm grew constantly more pleased as the name of each disease was called off, until at last they reached the end of the list, when some one proposed to make menstruation sometimes fatal to women. On this he rose-up in his place and cried: "*Wadâñ'!*

[Thanks!] I'm glad some more of them will die, for they are getting so thick that they tread on me." The thought fairly made him shake with joy, so that he fell over backward and could not get on his feet again, but had to wriggle off on his back, as the Grubworm has done ever since.

When the Plants, who were friendly to Man, heard what had been done by the animals, they determined to defeat the latter's evil designs. Each Tree, Shrub, and Herb, down even to the Grasses and Mosses, agreed to furnish a cure for some one of the diseases named, and each said: "I shall appear to help Man when he calls upon me in his need." Thus came medicine; and the plants, every one of which has its use if we only knew it, furnish the remedy to counteract the evil wrought by the revengeful animals. Even weeds were made for some good purpose, which we must find out for ourselves. When the doctor does not know what medicine to use for a sick man the spirit of the plant tells him.

A very great vision is needed and the man
who has it must follow it as the eagle seeks
the deepest blue of the sky.

Crazy Horse

The Daughter of the Sun

The Sun lived on the other side of the sky vault, but her daughter lived in the middle of the sky, directly above the earth, and every day as the Sun was climbing along the sky arch to the west she used to stop at her daughter's house for dinner.

Now, the Sun hated the people on the earth, because they could never look straight at her without screwing up their faces. She said to her brother, the Moon, "My grandchildren are ugly; they grin all over their faces when they look at me." But the Moon said, "I like my younger brothers; I think they are very handsome "--because they always smiled pleasantly when they saw him in the sky at night, for his rays were milder.

The Sun was jealous and planned to kill all the people, so every day when she got near her daughter's house she sent down such sultry rays that there was a great fever and the people died by hundreds, until everyone had lost some friend and there was fear that no one would be left. They went for help to the Little Men, who said the only way to save themselves was to kill the Sun.

The Little Men made medicine and changed two men to snakes, the Spreading-adder and the Copperhead, and sent them to watch near the door of the daughter of the Sun to bite the old Sun when she came next day. They went together and bid near the house until the Sun came, but when the Spreading-adder was about to spring, the bright light blinded him and he could only spit out yellow slime, as he does to this day when he tries to bite. She called him a nasty thing and went by into the house, and the Copperhead crawled off without trying to do anything.

So the people still died from the heat, and they went to the Little Men a second time for help. The Little Men made medicine again and changed one man into the great Uktena and another into the Rattlesnake and sent them to watch near the house and kill the old Sun when she came for dinner. They made the Uktena very large, with horns on his head, and everyone thought he would be sure to do the work, but the Rattlesnake was so quick and eager that he got ahead and coiled up just outside the house, and when the Sun's daughter opened the door to look out for her mother, he sprang up and bit her and she fell dead in the doorway. He forgot to wait for the old Sun, but went back to the people, and the Uktena was so very angry that he went back, too. Since then we pray to the rattlesnake and do not kill him, because he is kind and never tries to bite if we do not disturb him. The Uktena grew angrier all the time and very dangerous, so that if he even looked at a man, that man's family would die. After a long time the people held a council and decided that he was too dangerous to be with them, so they sent him up to Gälûñ'lätï, and he is there now. The Spreading-adder, the Copperhead, the Rattlesnake, and the Uktena were all men.

When the Sun found her daughter dead, she went into the house and grieved, and the people did not die any more, but now the world was dark all the time, because the Sun would not come out. They went again to the Little Men, and these told them that if they wanted the Sun to come out again they must bring back her daughter from Tsûsginâ'ï, the Ghost country, in Us'ûñhi'yï, the Darkening land in the west. They chose seven men to go, and gave each a sourwood rod a hand-breadth long. The Little Men told them they must take a box with them, and when they got to Tsûsginâ'ï they would find all the ghosts at a dance. They must stand outside the circle, and when the young woman passed in the dance they must strike her with the rods and she would fall to the ground. Then they must put her into the box and bring her back to her mother, but they must be very sure not to open the box, even a little way, until they were home again.

They took the rods and a box and traveled seven days to the west until they came to the Darkening land. There were a great many people there, and they were having a dance just as if they were at home in the settlements. The young woman was in the outside circle, and as she swung around to where the seven men were standing, one struck her with his rod and she turned her head and saw him. As she came around the second time another touched her with his rod, and then another and another, until at the seventh round she fell out of the ring, and they put her into the box and closed the lid fast. The other ghosts seemed never to notice what had happened.

They took up the box and started home toward the east. In a little while the girl came to life again and begged to be let out of the box, but they made no answer and went on. Soon she called again and said she was hungry, but still they made no answer and went on. After another while she spoke again and called for a drink and pleaded so that it was very hard to listen to her, but the men who carried the box said nothing and still went on. When at last they were very near home, she called again and begged them to raise the lid just a little, because she was smothering. They were afraid she was really dying now, so they lifted the lid a little to give her air, but as they did so there was a fluttering sound inside and something flew past them into the thicket and they heard a redbird cry, "*kwish! kwish! kwish!*" in the bushes. They shut down the lid and went on again to the settlements, but when they got there and opened the box it was empty.

So we know the Redbird is the daughter of the Sun, and if the men had kept the box closed, as the Little Men told them to do, they would have brought her home safely, and we could bring back our other friends also from the Ghost country, but now when they die we can never bring them back.

The Sun had been glad when they started to the Ghost country, but when they came back without her daughter she grieved and cried, "My daughter, my daughter," and wept until her tears made a flood upon the earth, and the people were afraid the world would be drowned. They held another council, and sent their handsomest young men and women to amuse her so that she would stop crying. They danced before the Sun and sang their best songs, but for a long time she kept her face covered and paid no attention, until at last the drummer suddenly changed the song, when she lifted up her face, and was so pleased at the sight that she forgot her grief and smiled.

The Journey to the Sunrise

A long time ago several young men made up their minds to find the place where the Sun lives and see what the Sun is like. They got ready their bows and arrows, their parched corn and extra moccasins, and started out toward the east. At first they met tribes they knew, then they came to tribes they had only heard about, and at last to others of which they had never heard.

There was a tribe of root eaters and another of acorn eaters, with great piles of acorn shells near their houses. In one tribe they found a sick man dying, and were told it was the custom there when a man died to bury his wife in the same grave with him. They waited until he was dead, when they saw his friends lower the body into a great pit, so deep and dark that from the top they could not see the bottom. Then a rope was tied around the woman's body, together with a bundle of pine knots, a lighted pine knot was put into her hand, and she was lowered into the pit to die there in the darkness after the last pine knot was burned.

The young men traveled on until they came at last to the sunrise place where the sky reaches down to the ground. They found that the sky was an arch or vault of solid rock hung above the earth and was always swinging up and down, so that when it went up there was an open place like a door between the sky and ground, and when it swung back the door was shut. The Sun came out of this door from the east and climbed along on the inside of the arch. It had a human figure, but was too bright for them to see clearly and too hot to come very near. They waited until the Sun had come out and then tried to get through while the door was still open, but just as the first one was in the doorway the rock came down and crushed him. The other six were afraid to try it, and as they were now at the end of the world they turned around and started back again, but they had traveled so far that they were old men when they reached home.

When a white army battles Indians and wins, it
is called a great victory, but if they lose it
is called a massacre.

Chiksika, Shawnee

What the Stars are like

There are different opinions about the stars. Some say they are balls of light, others say they are human, but most people say they are living creatures covered with luminous fur or feathers.

One night a hunting party camping in the mountains noticed two lights like large stars moving along the top of a distant ridge. They wondered and watched until the light disappeared on the other side. The next night, and the next, they saw the lights again moving along the ridge, and after talking over the matter decided to go on the morrow and try to learn the cause. In the morning they started out and went until they came to the ridge, where, after searching some time, they found two strange creatures about *so* large (making a circle with outstretched arms), with round bodies covered with fine fur or downy feathers, from which small heads stuck out like the heads of terrapins. As the breeze played upon these feathers showers of sparks flew out.

The hunters carried the strange creatures back to the camp, intending to take them home to the settlements on their return. They kept them several days and noticed that every night they would grow bright and shine like great stars, although by day they were only balls of gray fur, except when the wind stirred and made the sparks fly out. They kept very quiet, and no one thought of their trying to escape, when, on the seventh night, they suddenly rose from the ground like balls of fire and were soon above the tops of the trees. Higher and higher they went, while the wondering hunters watched, until at last they were only two bright points of light in the dark sky, and then the hunters knew that they were stars.

The Great Spirit Chief who rules above all
will smile upon this land...
and this time the Indian race is waiting and praying.

Chief Joseph

Origin of Strawberries

When the first man was created and a mate was given to him, they lived together very happily for a time, but then began to quarrel, until at last the woman left her husband and started off toward Nûñâgûñ'yï, the Sun land, in the east. The man followed alone and grieving, but the woman kept on steadily ahead and never looked behind, until Une''länûñ'hï, the great Apportioner (the Sun), took pity on him and asked him if he was still angry with his wife. He said he was not, and Une''länûñ'hï then asked him if he would like to have her back again, to which he eagerly answered yes.

So Une''länûñ'hï caused a patch of the finest ripe huckleberries to spring up along the path in front of the woman, but she passed by without paying any attention to them. Farther on he put a clump Of blackberries, but these also she refused to notice. Other fruits, one, two, and three, and then some trees covered with beautiful red service berries, were placed beside the path to tempt her, but she still went on until suddenly she saw in front a patch of large ripe strawberries, the first ever known. She stooped to gather a few to eat, and as she picked them she chanced to turn her face to the west, and at once the memory of her husband came back to her and she found herself unable to go on. She sat down, but the longer she waited the stronger became her desire, for her husband, and at last she gathered a bunch of the finest berries and started back along the path to give them to him. He met her kindly and they went home together.

The Deluge

A long time ago a man had a dog, which began to go down to the river every day and look at the water and howl. At last the man was angry and scolded the dog, which then spoke to him and said: "Very soon there is going to be a great freshet and the water will come so high that everybody will be drowned; but if you will make a raft to get upon when the rain comes you can be saved, but you must first throw me into the water." The man did not believe it, and the dog said, "If you want a sign that I speak the truth, look at the back of my neck." He looked and saw that the dog's neck had the skin worn off so that the bones stuck out.

Then he believed the dog, and began to build a raft. Soon the rain came and he took his family, with plenty of provisions and they all got upon it. It rained for a long time, and the water rose until the mountains were covered and all the people in the world were drowned. Then the rain stopped and the waters went down again, until at last it was safe to come off the raft. Now there was no one alive but the man and his family, but one day they heard a sound of dancing and shouting on the other side of the ridge. The man climbed to the top and looked over; everything was still, but all along the valley he saw great piles of bones of the people who had been drowned, and then he knew that the ghosts had been dancing.

How the Rabbit Stole the Otter's Coat

The animals were of different sizes and wore coats of various colors and patterns. Some wore long fur and others wore short. Some had rings on their tails, and some had no tails at all. Some had coats of brown, others of black or yellow. They were always disputing about their good looks, so at last they agreed to hold a council to decide who had the finest coat.

They had heard a great deal about the Otter, who lived so far up the creek that he seldom came down to visit the other animals. It was said that he had the finest coat of all, but no one knew just what it was like, because it was a long time since anyone had seen him. They did not even know exactly where he lived--only the general direction; but they knew he would come to the council when the word got out.

Now the Rabbit wanted the verdict for himself, so when it began to look as if it might go to the Otter he studied up a plan to cheat him out of it. He asked a few sly questions until he learned what trail the Otter would take to get to the council place. Then, without saying anything, he went on ahead and after four days' travel he met the Otter and knew him at once by his beautiful coat of soft dark-brown fur. The Otter was glad to see him and asked him where he was going.

"O," said the Rabbit, "the animals sent me to bring you to the council; because you live so far away they were afraid you mightn't know the road." The Otter thanked him, and they went on together.

They traveled all day toward the council ground, and at night the Rabbit selected the camping place, because the Otter was a stranger in that part of the country, and cut down bushes for beds and fixed everything in good shape. The next morning they started on again. In the afternoon the Rabbit began to pick up wood and bark as they went along and to load it on his back. When the Otter asked what this was for the Rabbit said it was that they might be warm and comfortable at night. After a while, when it was near sunset, they stopped and made their camp.

When supper was over the Rabbit got a stick and shaved it down to a paddle. The Otter wondered and asked again what that was for.

"I have good dreams when I sleep with a paddle under my head," said the Rabbit.

When the paddle was finished the Rabbit began to cut away the bushes so as to make a clean trail down to the river. The Otter wondered more and more and wanted to know what this meant.

Said the Rabbit, "This place is called Di'tatlâski'yï [The Place Where it Rains Fire]. Sometimes it rains fire here, and the sky looks a little that way to-night. You go to sleep and I'll sit up and watch, and if the fire does come, a soon as you hear me shout, you run and jump into the river. Better hang your coat on a limb over there, so it won't get burnt."

The Otter did as he was told, and they both doubled up to go to sleep, but the Rabbit kept awake. After a while the fire burned down to red coals. The Rabbit called, but the Otter was fast asleep and made no answer. In a little while he called again, but the Otter never stirred. Then the Rabbit filled the paddle with hot coals and threw them up into the air and shouted, "It's raining fire! It's raining fire!"

The hot coals fell all around the Otter and he jumped up. "To the water!" cried the Rabbit, and the Otter ran and jumped into the river, and he has lived in the water ever since.

The Rabbit took the Otter's coat and put it on, leaving his own instead, and went on to the council. All the animals were there, every one looking out for the Otter. At last they saw him in the distance, and they said one to the other, "The Otter is coming!" and sent one of the small animals to show him the best seat. They were all glad to see him and went up in turn to welcome him, but the Otter kept his head down, with one paw over his face. They wondered that he was so bashful, until the Bear came up and pulled the paw away, and there was the Rabbit with his split nose. He sprang up and started to run, when the Bear struck at him and pulled his tail off, but the Rabbit was too quick for them and got away.

Why the Possum's Tail is Bare

The Possum used to have a long, bushy tail, and was so proud of it that he combed it out every morning and sang about it at the dance, until the Rabbit, who had had no tail since the Bear pulled it out, became very jealous and made up his mind to play the Possum a trick.

There was to be a great council and a dance at which all the animals were to be present. It was the Rabbit's business to send out the news, so as he was passing the Possum's place he stopped to ask him if he intended to be there. The Possum said he would come if he could have a special seat, "because I have such a handsome tail that I ought to sit where everybody can see me." The Rabbit promised to attend to it and to send some one besides to comb and dress the Possum's tail for the dance, so the Possum was very much pleased and agreed to come.

Then the Rabbit went over to the Cricket, who is such an expert hair cutter that the Indians call him the barber, and told him to go next morning and dress the Possum's tail for the dance that night. He told the Cricket just what to do and then went on about some other mischief.

In the morning the Cricket went to the Possum's house and said he had come to get him ready for the dance. So the Possum stretched himself out and shut his eyes while the Cricket combed out his tail and wrapped a red string around it to keep it smooth until night. But all this time, as he wound the string around, he was clipping off the hair close to the roots, and the Possum never knew it.

When it was night the Possum went to the townhouse where the dance was to be and found the best seat ready for him, just as the Rabbit had promised. When his turn came in the dance he loosened the string from his tail and stepped into the middle of the floor. The drummers began to drum and the Possum began to sing, "See my beautiful tail." Everybody shouted and he danced around the circle and sang again, "See what a fine color it has." They shouted again and he danced around another time, singing, "See how it sweeps the ground." The animals shouted more loudly than ever, and the Possum was delighted. He danced around again and sang, "See how fine the fur is." Then everybody laughed so long that the Possum wondered what they meant. He looked around the circle of animals and they were all laughing at him. Then he looked down at his beautiful tail and saw that there was not a hair left upon it, but that it was as bare as the tail of a lizard. He was so much astonished and ashamed that he could not say a word, but rolled over helpless on the ground and grinned, as the Possum does to this day when taken by surprise.

How the Wildcat Caught the Gobbler

The Wildcat once caught the Rabbit and was about to kill him, when the Rabbit begged for his life, saying: "I'm so small I would make only a mouthful for you, but if you let me go I'll show you where you can get a whole drove of Turkeys." So the Wildcat let him up and went with him to where the Turkeys were.

When they came near the place the Rabbit said to the Wildcat,

Now, you must do just as I say. Lie down as if you were dead and don't move, even if I kick you, but when I give, the word jump up and catch the large stone there." The Wildcat agreed and stretched out as if dead, while the Rabbit gathered some rotten wood and crumbled it over his eyes and nose to make them look flyblown, so that the Turkeys would think he had been dead some time.

Then the Rabbit went over to the Turkeys and said, in a sociable way, "Here, I've found our old enemy, the Wildcat, lying dead in the trail. Let's have a dance over him." The Turkeys were very doubtful, but finally went with him to where the Wildcat was lying in the road as if dead. Now, the Rabbit had a good voice and was a great dance leader, so he said, "I'll lead the song and you dance around him." The Turkeys thought that fine, so the Rabbit took a stick to beat time and began to sing: "*Gälägi'na hasuyak'*, *Gälägi'na hasuyak'* (pick out the Gobbler, pick out the Gobbler)."

"Why do you say that?" said the old Turkey. "O, that's all right," said the Rabbit, "that's just the way he does, and we sing about it."

He started the song again and the Turkeys began to dance around the Wildcat. When they had gone around several times the Rabbit said, "Now go up and hit him, as we do in the war dance." So the Turkeys, thinking the Wildcat surely dead, crowded in close around him and the old gobbler kicked him. Then the Rabbit drummed hard and sang his loudest, "Pick out the Gobbler, pick out the Gobbler," and the Wildcat jumped up and caught the Gobbler.

We are now about to take our leave and kind farewell to our native land, the country the Great Spirit gave our Fathers, we are on the eve of leaving that country that gave us birth, it is with sorrow we are forced by the white man to quit the scenes of our childhood...we bid farewell to it and all we hold dear.

Charles Hicks, Tsalagi (Cherokee) Vice Chief speaking of The Trail of Tears, Nov. 4, 1838

How the Terrapin Beat the Rabbit

The Rabbit was a great runner, and everybody knew it. No one thought the Terrapin anything but a slow traveler, but he was a great warrior and very boastful, and the two were always disputing about their speed. At last they agreed to decide the matter by a race. They fixed the day and the starting place and arranged to run across four mountain ridges, and the one who came in first at the end was to be the winner.

The Rabbit felt so sure of it that he said to the Terrapin, "You know you can't run. You can never win the race, so I'll give you the first ridge and then you'll have only three to cross while I go over four."

The Terrapin said that would be all right, but that night when he went home to his family he sent for his Terrapin friends and told them he wanted their help. He said he knew he could not outrun the Rabbit, but he wanted to stop the Rabbit's boasting. He explained his plan to his friends and they agreed to help him.

When the day came all the animals were there to see the race. The Rabbit was with them, but the Terrapin was gone ahead toward the first ridge, as they had arranged, and they could hardly see him on account of the long grass. The word was given and the Rabbit started off with long jumps up the mountain, expecting to win the race before the Terrapin could get down the other side. But before he got up the mountain he saw the Terrapin go over the ridge ahead of him. He ran on, and when he reached the top he looked all around, but could not see the Terrapin on account of the long grass. He kept on down the mountain and began to climb the second ridge, but when he looked up again there was the Terrapin just going over the top. Now he was surprised and made his longest jumps to catch up, but when he got to the top there was the Terrapin away in front going over the third ridge. The Rabbit was getting tired now and nearly out of breath, but he kept on down the mountain and up the other ridge until he got to the top just in time to see the Terrapin cross the fourth ridge and thus win the race.

The Rabbit could not make another jump, but fell over on the ground, crying *mï, mï, mï, mï,* as the Rabbit does ever since when he is too tired to run any more. The race was given to the Terrapin and all the animals wondered how he could win against the Rabbit, but he kept still and never told. It was easy enough, however, because all the Terrapin's friends looked just alike, and he had simply posted one near the top of each ridge to wait until the Rabbit came in sight and then climb over and hide in the long grass. When the Rabbit came on he could not find the Terrapin and so thought the Terrapin was ahead, and if he had met one of the other terrapins he would have thought it the same one because they looked so much alike. The real Terrapin had posted himself on the fourth ridge, so as to come in at the end of the race and be ready to answer questions if the animals suspected anything.

Because the Rabbit had to lie down and lose the race the conjurer now, when preparing his young men for the ball play, boils a lot of rabbit hamstrings into a soup, and sends some one at night to pour it across the path along which the other players are to come in the morning, so that they may become tired in the same way and lose the game. It is not always easy to do this, because the other party is expecting it and has watchers ahead to prevent it.

The Rabbit Dines the Bear

The Bear invited the Rabbit to dine with him. They had beans in the pot, but there was no grease for them, so the Bear cut a slit in his side and let the oil run out until they had enough to cook the dinner. The Rabbit looked surprised, and thought to himself, "That's a handy way. I think I'll try that. "When he started home he invited the Bear to come and take dinner with him four days later.

When the Bear came the Rabbit said, "I have beans for dinner, too. Now I'll get the grease for them." So he took a knife and drove it into his side, but instead of oil, a stream of blood gushed out and he fell over nearly dead. The Bear picked him up and had hard work to tie up the wound and stop the bleeding. Then he scolded him, "You little fool, I'm large and strong and lined with fat all over; the knife don't hurt me; but you're small and lean, and you can't do such things."

"One does not sell the land people walk on." ...

Crazy Horse, Sept. 23, 1875

The Rabbit Escapes from the Wolves

Some Wolves once caught the Rabbit and were going to eat him when he asked leave to show them a new dance he was practicing. They knew that the Rabbit was a great song leader, and they wanted to learn the latest dance, so they agreed and made a ring about him while he got ready.

He patted his feet and began to dance around in a circle, singing:

Tlâge'sitûñ' gäli'sgi'sidâ'hä--
Ha'nia lïl lïl! Ha'nia lïl lïl!

On the edge of the field I dance about--
Ha'nia lïl lïl! Ha'nia lïl lïl!

"Now, said the Rabbit, "when I sing 'on the edge of the field,' I dance that way"--and he danced over in that direction--"and when I sing lïl lïl! you must all stamp your feet hard." The Wolves thought it fine. He began another round singing the same song, and danced a little nearer to the field, while the Wolves all stamped their feet. He sang louder and louder and danced nearer and nearer to the field until at the fourth song, when the Wolves were stamping as hard as they could and thinking only of the song, he made one jump and was off through the long grass. They were after him at once, but he ran for a hollow stump and climbed up on the inside. When the Wolves got there one of them put his head inside to look up, but the Rabbit spit into his eye, so that he had to pull his head out again. The others were afraid to try, and they went away, with the Rabbit still in the stump.

Flint Visits the Rabbit

In the old days Täwi'skälä (Flint) lived up in the mountains, and all the animals hated him because he had helped to kill so many of them. They used to get together to talk over means to put him out of the way, but everybody was afraid to venture near his house until the Rabbit, who was the boldest leader among them, offered to go after Flint and try to kill him. They told him where to find him, and the Rabbit set out and at last came to Flint's house.

Flint was standing at his door when the Rabbit came up and said, sneeringly, "*Siyu'!* Hello! Are you the fellow they call Flint?" "Yes; that's what they call me," answered Flint. "Is this where you live?" "Yes; this is where I live." All this time the Rabbit was looking about the place trying to study out some plan to take Flint off his guard. He had expected Flint to invite him into the house, so he waited a little while, but when Flint made no move, he said, "Well, my name is Rabbit; I've heard a good deal about you, so I came to invite you to come and see me."

Flint wanted to know where the Rabbit's house was, and he told him it was down in the broom-grass field near the river. So Flint promised to make him a visit in a few days. "Why not come now and have supper with me?" said the Rabbit, and after a little coaxing Flint agreed and the two started down the mountain together.

When they came near the Rabbit's hole the Rabbit said, "There is my house, but in summer I generally stay outside here where it is cooler." So he made a fire, and they had their supper on the grass. When it was over, Flint stretched out to rest and the Rabbit got some heavy sticks and his knife and cut out a mallet and wedge. Flint looked up and asked what that was for. "Oh," said the Rabbit, "I like to be doing something, and they may come handy." So Flint lay down again, and pretty soon he was sound asleep. The Rabbit spoke to him once or twice to make sure, but there was no answer. Then he came over to Flint and with one good blow of the mallet he drove the sharp stake into his body and ran with all his might for his own hole; but before he reached it there was a loud explosion, and pieces of flint flew all about. That is why we find flint in so many places now. One piece struck the Rabbit from behind and cut him just as he dived into his hole. He sat listening until everything seemed quiet again. Then he put his head out to look around, but just at that moment another piece fell and struck him on the lip and split it, as we still see it.

The ground on which we stand is sacred ground. It is the dust and blood of our ancestors.

- Chief Plenty Coups, Crow (1848 - 1932)

How the Deer got his Horns

In the beginning the Deer had no horns, but his head was smooth just like a doe's. He was a great runner and the Rabbit was a great jumper, and the animals were all curious to know which could go farther in the same time. They talked about it a good deal, and at last arranged a match between the two, and made a nice large pair of antlers for a prize to the winner. They were to start together from one side of a thicket and go through it, then turn and come back, and the one who came out first was to get the horns.

On the day fixed all the animals were there, with the antlers put down on the ground at the edge of the thicket to mark the starting point. While everybody was admiring the horns the Rabbit said: "I don't know this part of the country; I want to take a look through the bushes where I am to run." They thought that all right, so the Rabbit went into the thicket, but he was gone so long that at last the animals suspected he must be up to one of his tricks. They sent a messenger to look for him, and away in the middle of the thicket he found the Rabbit gnawing down the bushes and pulling them away until he had a road cleared nearly to the other side.

The messenger turned around quietly and came back and told the other animals. When the Rabbit came out at last they accused him of cheating, but he denied it until they went into the thicket and found the cleared road. They agreed that such a trickster had no right to enter the race at all, so they gave the horns to the Deer, who was admitted to be the best runner, and he has worn them ever since. They told the Rabbit that as he was so fond of cutting down bushes he might do that for a living hereafter, and so he does to this day.

In our every deliberation, we must consider the impact of our decisions on the next seven generations.

- Iroquois Maxim (circa 1700-1800)

Why the Deer's Teeth are Blunt

The Rabbit felt sore because the Deer had won the horns, and resolved to get even. One day soon after the race he stretched a large grapevine across the trail and gnawed it nearly in two in the middle. Then he went back a piece, took a good run, and jumped up at the vine. He kept on running and jumping up at the vine until the Deer came along and asked him what he was doing?

"Don't you see?" says the Rabbit. "I'm so strong that I can bite through that grapevine at one jump."

The Deer could hardly believe this, and wanted to see it done.. So the Rabbit ran back, made a tremendous spring, and bit through the vine where he had gnawed it before. The Deer, when he saw that, said, "Well, I can do it if you can." So the Rabbit stretched a larger grapevine across the trail, but without gnawing it in the middle.

Deer ran back as he had seen the Rabbit do, made a spring, and struck the grapevine right in the center, but it only flew back and threw him over on his head. He tried again and again, until he was all bruised and bleeding.

"Let me see your teeth," at last said the Rabbit. So the Deer showed him his teeth, which were long like a wolf's teeth, but not very sharp.

"No wonder you can't do it," says the Rabbit; "your teeth are too blunt to bite anything. Let me sharpen them for you like mine. My

teeth are so sharp that I can cut through a stick just like a knife."
And he showed him a black locust twig, of which rabbits gnaw the
young shoots, which he had shaved off as well as a knife could do
it, in regular rabbit fashion. The Deer thought that just the thing.
So the Rabbit got a hard stone with rough edges and filed and filed
away at the Deer's teeth until they were worn down almost to the
gums.

"It hurts," said the Deer; but the Rabbit said it always hurt a little
when they began to get sharp; so the Deer kept quiet.

"Now try it," at last said the Rabbit. So the Deer tried again, but
this time he could not bite at all.

"Now you've paid for your horns," said the Rabbit, as he jumped
away through the bushes. Ever since then the Deer's teeth are so
blunt that he can not chew anything but grass and leaves.

Sometimes I go about pitying myself, and all the while I am being
carried across the sky by beautiful clouds.

Ojibway Proverb

What Became of the Rabbit

The Deer was very angry at the Rabbit for filing his teeth and determined to be revenged, but he kept still and pretended to be friendly until the Rabbit was off his guard. Then one day, as they were going along together talking, he challenged the Rabbit to jump against him. Now the Rabbit is a great jumper, as every one knows, so he agreed at once. There was a small stream beside the path, as there generally is in that country, and the Deer said:

"Let's see if you can jump across this branch. We'll go back a piece, and then when I say *Kû!* then both run and jump."

"All right," said the Rabbit. So they went back to get a good start, and when the Deer gave the word *Kû!* they ran for the stream, and the Rabbit made one jump and landed on the other side. But the Deer had stopped on the bank, and when the Rabbit looked back the Deer had conjured the stream so that it was a large river. The Rabbit was never able to get back again and is still on the other side. The rabbit that we know is only a little thing that came afterwards.

Why the Mole Lives Underground

A man was in love with a woman who disliked him and would have nothing to do with him. He tried every way to win her favor, but to no purpose, until at last he grew discouraged and made himself sick thinking over it. The Mole came along, and finding him in such low condition asked what was the trouble. The man told him the whole story, and when he had finished the Mole said: "I can help you, so that she will not only like you, but will come to you of her own will."

So that night the Mole burrowed his way underground to where the girl was in bed asleep and took out her heart. He came back by the same way and gave the heart to the man, who could not see it even when it was put into his hand. "There," said the Mole, "swallow it, and she will be drawn to come to you and can not keep away." The man swallowed the heart, and when the girl woke up she somehow thought at once of him, and felt a strange desire to be with him, as though she must go to him at once. She wondered and could not understand it, because she had always disliked him before, but at last the feeling grew so strong that she was compelled to go herself to the man and tell him she loved him and wanted to be his wife. And so they were married, but all the magicians who had known them both were surprised and wondered how it had come about. When they found that it was the work of the Mole, whom they had always before thought too insignificant for their notice, they were very jealous and threatened to kill him, so that he hid himself under the ground and has never since dared to come up to the surface.

The Terrapin's Escape from the Wolves

The Possum and the Terrapin went out together to hunt persimmons, and found a tree full of ripe fruit. The Possum climbed it and was throwing down the persimmons to the Terrapin when a wolf came up and began to snap at the persimmons as they fell, before the Terrapin could reach them.

The Possum waited his chance, and at last managed to throw down a large one (some say a bone which he carried with him), so that it lodged in the wolf's throat as he jumped up at it and choked him to death. "I'll take his ears for hominy spoons," said the Terrapin, and cut off the wolf's ears and started home with them, leaving the Possum still eating persimmons up in the tree.

After a while he came to a house and was invited to have some *kanahe'na* gruel from the jar that is set always outside the door. He sat down beside the jar and dipped up the gruel with one of the wolf's ears for a spoon. The people noticed and wondered. When he was satisfied he went on, but soon came to another house and was asked to have some more kanahe'na. He dipped it up again with the wolf's ear and went on when he had enough.

Soon the news went around, that the Terrapin had killed the Wolf and was using his ears for spoons. All the Wolves got together and followed the Terrapin's trail until they came up with him and made him prisoner. Then they held a council to decide what to do with him, and agreed to boil him in a clay pot.

They brought in a pot, but the Terrapin only laughed at it and said that if they put him into that thing he would kick it all to pieces. They said they would burn him in the fire, but the Terrapin laughed again and said he would put it out. Then they decided to throw him into the deepest hole in the river and drown him. The Terrapin begged and prayed them not to do that, but they paid no attention, and dragged him over to the river and threw him in. That was just what the Terrapin had been waiting for all the time, and he dived under the water and came up on the other side and got away.

Some say that when he was thrown into the river he struck against a rock, which broke, his back in a dozen places. He sang a medicine song:

> *Gû'daye'wû, Gû'daye'wû,*
> I have sewed myself together, I have sewed myself together,

and the pieces came together, but the scars remain on his shell to this day.

Origin of the Groundhog Dance: The Groundhog's Head

Seven wolves once caught a Groundhog and said, "Now we'll kill you and have something good to eat." But the Groundhog said, "When we find good food we must rejoice over it, as people do in the Green-corn dance. I know you mean to kill me and I can't help myself, but if you want to dance I'll sing for you. This is a new dance entirely. I'll lean up against seven trees in turn and you will dance out and then turn and come back, as I give the signal, and at the last turn you may kill me."

The wolves were very hungry, but they wanted to learn the new dance, so they told him to go ahead. The Groundhog leaned up against a tree and began the song, *Ha'wiy'ëhï'*, and all the wolves danced out in front, until he gave the signal, *Yu!* and began with *Ha'wiy'ëhï'*, when they turned and danced back in line. "That's fine," said the Groundhog, and went over to the next tree and started the second song. The wolves danced, out and then turned at the signal and danced back again. "That's very fine," said the Groundhog, and went over to another tree and started the third song. The wolves danced their best and the Groundhog encouraged them, but at each song he took another tree, and each tree was a little nearer to his hole under a stump. At the seventh song he said, "Now, this is the last dance, and when I say *Yu!* you will all turn and come after me, and the one who gets me may have me." So he began the seventh song and kept it up until the wolves were away out in front. Then he gave the signal, *Yu!* and made a jump for his hole. The wolves turned and were after him, but he reached the hole first and dived in. Just as he got inside, the foremost wolf caught him by the tail and gave it such a pull that it broke off, and the Groundhog's tail has been short ever since.

$$* \quad * \quad * \quad * \quad * \quad * \quad *$$

The unpleasant smell of the Groundhog's head was given it by the other animals to punish an insulting remark made by him in council. The story is a vulgar one, without wit enough to make it worth recording.

The Wolf's Revenge--the Wolf and the Dog

Kana'tï had wolves to hunt for him, because they are good hunters and never fail. He once sent out two wolves at once. One went to the east and did not return. The other went to the north, and when he returned at night and did not find his fellow he knew he must be in trouble and started after him. After traveling on some time he found his brother lying nearly dead beside a great greensnake (*sälikwa'yâ'yï*) which had attacked him. The snake itself was too badly wounded to crawl away, and the angry wolf, who had magic powers, taking out several hairs from his own whiskers, shot them into the body of the snake and killed it. He then hurried back to Kana'tï, who sent the Terrapin after a great doctor who lived in the west to save the wounded wolf. The wolf went back to help his brother and by his magic powers he had him cured long before the doctor came from the west, because the Terrapin was such a slow traveler and the doctor had to prepare his roots before he started.

*   *   *   *   *   *   *

In the beginning, the people say, the Dog was put on the mountain and the Wolf beside the fire. When the winter came the Dog could not stand the cold, so he came down to the settlement and drove the Wolf from the fire. The Wolf ran to the mountains, where it suited him so well that he prospered and increased, until after a while he ventured down again and killed some animals in the settlements. The people got together and followed and killed him, but his brothers came from the mountains and took such revenge that ever since the people have been afraid to hurt a wolf.

The life of an Indian is like the wings of the air. That is why you notice the hawk knows how to get his prey. The Indian is like that. The hawk swoops down on its prey, so does the Indian. In his lament he is like an animal. For instance, the coyote is sly, so is the Indian. The eagle is the same. That is why the Indian is always feathered up, he is a relative to the wings of the air.

- Black Elk, Oglala Lakota Sioux (1863-1950)

How the Turkey got his Beard

When the Terrapin won the race from the Rabbit all the animals wondered and talked about it a great deal, because they had always thought the Terrapin slow, although they knew that he was a warrior and had many conjuring secrets beside. But the Turkey was not satisfied and told the others there must be some trick about it. Said he, "I know the Terrapin can't run--he can hardly crawl--and I'm going to try him."

So one day the Turkey met the Terrapin coming home from war with a fresh scalp hanging from his neck and dragging on the ground as he traveled. The Turkey laughed at the sight and said: "That scalp don't look right on you. Your neck is too short and low down to wear it that way. Let me show you."

The Terrapin agreed and gave the scalp to the Turkey, who fastened it around his neck. "Now," said the Turkey, "I'll walk a little way and you can see how it looks." So he walked ahead a short distance and then turned and asked the Terrapin how he liked it. Said the Terrapin, "It looks very nice; it becomes you."

"Now I'll fix it in a different way and let you see how it looks," said the Turkey. So he gave the string another pull and walked ahead again. "O, that looks very nice," said the Terrapin. But the Turkey kept on walking, and when the Terrapin called to him to bring back the scalp he only walked faster and broke into a run. Then the Terrapin got out his bow and by his conjuring art shot a number of cane splints into the Turkey's leg to cripple him so that he could not run, which accounts for all the many small bones in the Turkey's leg, that are of no use whatever; but the Terrapin never caught the Turkey, who still wears the scalp from his neck.

Why the Turkey Gobbles

The Grouse used to have a fine voice and a good halloo in the ballplay. All the animals and birds used to play ball in those days and were just as proud of a loud halloo as the ball players of to-day. The Turkey had not a good voice, so he asked the Grouse to

give him lessons. The Grouse agreed to teach him, but wanted pay for his trouble, and the Turkey promised to give him some feathers to make himself a collar. That is how the Grouse got his collar of turkey feathers. They began the lessons and the Turkey learned very fast until the Grouse thought it was time to try his voice. "Now," said the Grouse, "I'll stand on this hollow log, and when I give the signal by tapping on it, you must halloo as loudly as you can." So he got upon the log ready to tap on it, as a Grouse does, but when he gave the signal the Turkey was so eager and excited that he could not raise his voice for a shout, but only gobbled, and ever since then he gobbles whenever he hears a noise.

How the Redbird got his Color

A Raccoon passing a Wolf one day made several insulting remarks, until at last the Wolf became angry and turned and chased him. The Raccoon ran his best and managed to reach a tree by the river side before the Wolf came up. He climbed the tree and stretched out on a limb overhanging the water. When the Wolf arrived he saw the reflection in the water, and thinking it was the Raccoon he jumped at it and was nearly drowned before he could scramble out again, all wet and dripping. He lay down on the bank to dry and fell asleep. and while he was sleeping the Raccoon came down the tree and plastered his eves with dung. When the Wolf awoke he found he could not open his eyes, and began to whine. Along came a little brown and through the bushes and beard the Wolf crying and asked what was the matter. The Wolf told his story and said, "If you will get my eyes open, I will show you where to find some nice red paint to paint yourself." "All right," said the brown bird; so he pecked at the Wolf's eyes until he got off all the plaster. Then the Wolf took him to a rock that had streaks of bright red paint running through it, and the little bird painted himself with it, and has ever since been a Redbird.

The Pheasant Beating Corn; Origin of the Pheasant Dance

The Pheasant once saw a woman beating corn in a wooden mortar in front of the house. "I can do that, too," said he, but the woman would not believe it, so the Pheasant went into the woods and got upon a hollow log and "drummed" with his wings as a pheasant does, until the people in the house heard him and thought he was really beating corn.

*   *   *   *   *   *   *

In the Pheasant dance, a part of the Green-corn dance, the instrument used is the drum, and the dancers beat the ground with their feet in imitation of the drumming sound made by the pheasant. They form two concentric circles, the men being on the inside, facing the women in the outer circle, each in turn advancing and retreating at the signal of the drummer, who sits at one side and sings the Pheasant songs. According to the story, there was once a winter famine among the birds and animals. No mast (fallen nuts) could be found in the woods, and they were near starvation when a Pheasant discovered a holly tree, loaded with red berries, of which the Pheasant is said to be particularly fond. He called his companion birds, and they formed a circle about the tree, singing, dancing, and drumming with their wings in token of their joy, and thus originated the Pheasant dance.

The Race Between the Crane and the Hummingbird

The Hummingbird and the Crane were both in love with a pretty woman. She preferred the Hummingbird, who was as handsome as the Crane was awkward, but the Crane was so persistent that in order to get rid of him she finally told him he must challenge the other to a race and she would marry the winner. The Hummingbird was so swift--almost like a flash of lightning--and the Crane so slow and heavy, that she felt sure the Hummingbird would win. She did not know the Crane could fly all night.

They agreed to start from her house and fly around the circle of the world to the beginning, and the one who came in first would marry the woman. At the word the Hummingbird darted off like an arrow and was out of sight in a moment, leaving his rival to follow heavily behind. He flew all day, and when evening came and he stopped to roost for the night he was far ahead. But the Crane flew steadily all night long, passing the Hummingbird soon after midnight and going on until he came to a creek and stopped to rest about daylight. The Hummingbird woke up in the morning and flew on again, thinking how easily he would win the race, until he reached the creek and there found the Crane spearing tadpoles, with his long bill, for breakfast. He was very much surprised and wondered how this could have happened, but he flew swiftly by and soon left the Crane out of sight again.

The Crane finished his breakfast and started on, and when evening came he kept on as before. This time it was hardly midnight when he passed the Hummingbird asleep on a limb, and in the morning he had finished his breakfast before the other came up. The next day he gained a little more, and on the fourth day he was spearing tadpoles for dinner when the Hummingbird passed him. On the fifth and sixth days it was late in the afternoon before the Hummingbird came up, and on the morning of the seventh day the Crane was ' a whole night's travel ahead. He took his time at breakfast and then fixed himself up as nicely as he could at the creek and came in at the starting place where the woman lived, early in the morning. When the Hummingbird arrived in the afternoon he found he had lost the race, but the woman declared she would never have such an ugly fellow as the Crane for a husband, so she stayed single.

The Owl Gets Married

A widow with one daughter was always warning the girl that she must be sure to get a good hunter for a husband when she married. The young woman listened and promised to do as her mother advised. At last a suitor came to ask the mother for the girl, but the widow told him that only a good hunter could have her daughter. "I'm just that kind," said the lover, and again asked her to speak for him to the young woman. So the mother went to the girl and told her a young man had come a-courting, and as he said he was a good hunter she advised her daughter to take him. "Just as you say," said the girl. So when he came again the matter was all arranged, and he went to live with the girl.

The next morning he got ready and said he would go out hunting, but before starting he changed his mind and said he would go fishing. He was gone all day and came home late at night, bringing only three small fish, saying that he had had no luck, but would have better success to-morrow. The next morning he started off again to fish and was gone all day, but came home at night with only two worthless spring lizards (*duwë'gä*) and the same excuse. Next day he said he would go hunting this time. He was gone again until night, and returned at last with only a handful of scraps that he had found where some hunters had cut up a deer.

By this time the old woman was suspicious. So next morning when he started off again, as he said, to fish, she told her daughter to follow him secretly and see how he set to work. The girl followed through the woods and kept him in sight until he came down to the river, where she saw her husband change to a hooting owl (*uguku'*) and fly over to a pile of driftwood in the water and cry, "*U-gu-ku! hu! hu! u! u!*" She was surprised and very angry and said to herself, "I thought I had married a man, but my husband is only an owl." She watched and saw the owl look into the water for a long time and at last swoop down and bring up in his claws a handful of sand, from which he picked out a crawfish. Then he flew across to the bank, took the form of a man again, and started home with the crawfish. His wife hurried on ahead through the woods and got there before him. When he came in with the crawfish in his hand, she asked him where, were all the fish he had caught. He said he had none, because an owl had frightened them all away. "I think you are the owl," said his wife, and drove him out of the house. The owl went into the woods and there he pined away with grief and love until there was no flesh left on any part of his body except his head.

The Huhu Gets Married

A widow who had an only daughter, but no son, found it very hard to make a living and was constantly urging upon the young woman that they ought to have a man in the family, who would be a good hunter and able to help in the field. One evening a stranger lover came courting to the house, and when the girl told him that she could marry only one who was a good worker, he declared that he was exactly that sort of man; so the girl talked to her mother, and on her advice they were married.

The next morning the widow gave her new son-in-law a hoe and sent him out to the cornfield. When breakfast was ready she went to call him, following a sound as of some one hoeing on stony soil, but when she came to the spot she found only a small circle of hoed ground and no sign of her son-in-law. Away over in the thicket she heard a huhu calling.

He did not come in for dinner, either, and when he returned home in the evening the old woman asked him where he had been all day. "Hard at work," said he. "But I didn't see you when I came to call you to breakfast." "I was down in the thicket cutting sticks to mark off the field," said he. "But why didn't you come in to dinner?" "I was too busy working," said he. So the old woman was satisfied, and they had their supper together.

Early next morning he started off with his hoe over his shoulder. When breakfast was ready the old woman went again to call him, but found no sign of him, only the hoe lying there and no work done. And away over in the thicket a huhu was calling, *"Sau-h! sau-h! sau-h! hu! hu! hu! hu! hu! hu! chi! chi! chi!--whew!"*

She went back to the house, and when at last he came home in the evening she asked him again what he had been doing all day. "Working hard," said he. "But you were not there when I came after you." "O, I just went over in the thicket a while to see some of my kinsfolk," said he. Then the old woman said, "I have lived here a long time and there is nothing living in the swamp but huhus. My daughter wants a husband that can work and not a lazy huhu; so you may go." And she drove him from the house.

Why the Buzzard's Head is Bare

The buzzard used to have a fine topknot, of which he was so proud that he refused to eat carrion, and while the other birds were pecking at the body of a deer or other animal which they had found he would strut around and say: "You may have it all, it is not good enough for me." They resolved to punish him, and with the help of the buffalo carried out a plot by which the buzzard lost not his topknot alone, but nearly all the other feathers on his head. He lost his pride at the same time, so that he is willing enough now to eat carrion for a living.

The Eagle's Revenge

Once a hunter in the mountains heard a noise at night like a rushing wind outside the cabin, and on going out he found that an eagle had just alighted on the drying pole and was tearing at the body of a deer hanging there. Without thinking of the danger, he shot the eagle. In the morning he took the deer and started back to the settlement, where he told what he had done, and the chief sent out some men to bring in the eagle and arrange for an Eagle dance. They brought back the dead eagle, everything was made ready, and that night they started the dance in the townhouse.

About midnight there was a whoop outside and a strange warrior came into the circle and began to recite his exploits. No one knew him, but they thought he had come from one of the farther Cherokee towns. He told how he had killed a man, and at the end of the story he gave a hoarse yell, *Hi!* that startled the whole company, and one of the seven men with the rattles fell over dead. He sang of another deed, and at the end straightened up with another loud yell. A second rattler fell dead, and the people were so full of fear that they could not stir from their places. Still he kept on, and at every pause there came again that terrible scream, until the last of the seven rattlers fell dead, and then the stranger went out into the darkness. Long afterward they learned from the eagle killer that it was the brother of the eagle shot by the hunter.

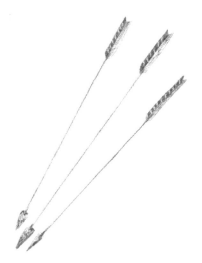

The Hunter and the Buzzard

A hunter had been all day looking for deer in the mountains without success until he was completely tired out and sat down on a log to rest and wonder what he should do, when a buzzard--a bird which always has magic powers--came flying overhead and spoke to him, asking him what was his trouble. When the hunter had told his story the buzzard said there were plenty of deer on the ridges beyond if only the hunter were high up in the air where he could see them, and proposed that they exchange forms for a while, when the buzzard would go home to the hunter's wife while the hunter would go to look for deer. The hunter agreed, and the buzzard became a man and went home to the hunter's wife, who received him as her husband, while the hunter became a buzzard and flew off over the mountain to locate the deer. After staying some time with the woman, who thought always it was her real husband, the buzzard excused himself, saying he must go again to look for game or they would have nothing to eat. He came to the place where he had first met the hunter, and found him already there, still in buzzard form, awaiting him. He asked the hunter what success he had had, and the hunter replied that he had found several deer over the ridge, as the buzzard had said. Then the buzzard restored the hunter to human shape, and became himself a buzzard again and flew away. The hunter went where he had seen the deer and killed several, and from that time he never returned empty-handed from the woods.

The Red Man and the Uktena

Two brothers went bunting together, and when they came to a good camping place in the mountains they made a fire, and while one gathered bark to put up a shelter the other started up the creek to look for a deer. Soon he heard a noise on the top of the ridge as if two animals were fighting. He hurried through the bushes to see what it might be, and when he came to the spot he found a great uktena coiled around a man and choking him to death. The man was fighting for his life, and called out to the hunter: "Help me, nephew; he is your enemy as well as mine." The hunter took good aim, and, drawing the arrow to the head, sent it through the body of the uktena, so that the blood spouted from the hole. The snake loosed its coils with a snapping noise, and went tumbling down the ridge into the valley, tearing up the earth like a water spout as it rolled..

The stranger stood up, and it was the Asga'ya Gi'gägeï, the Red Man of the Lightning. He said to the hunter: "You have helped me, and now I will reward you, and give you a medicine so that you can always find game." They waited until it was dark, and then went down the ridge to where the dead uktena had rolled, but by this time the birds and insects had eaten the body and only the bones were left. In one place were flashes of light coming up from the ground, and on digging here, just under the surface, the Red Man found a scale of the uktena. Next he went over to a tree that had been struck by lightning, and gathering a handful of splinters he made a fire and burned the uktena scale to a coal. He wrapped this in a piece of deerskin and gave it to the hunter, saying: "As long as you keep this you can always kill game." Then he told the hunter that when he went back to camp he must hang up the medicine on a tree outside, because it was very strong and dangerous. He told him also that when he went into the cabin he would find his brother lying inside nearly dead on account of the presence of the uktena's scale, but he must take a small piece of cane, which the Red Man gave him, and scrape a little of it into water and give it to his brother to drink and he would be well again. Then the Red Man was gone, and the hunter could not see where he went. He returned to camp alone, and found his brother very sick, but soon cured him with the medicine from the cane, and that, day and the next, and every day after, he found game whenever he went for it.

The Snake Boy

There was a boy who used to go bird hunting every day, and all the birds he brought home he gave to his grandmother, who was very fond of him. This made the rest of the family jealous, and they treated him in such fashion that at last one day he told his grandmother he would leave them all, but that she must not grieve for him. Next morning he refused to eat any breakfast, but went off hungry to the woods and was gone all day. In the evening he returned, bringing with him a pair of deer horns, and went directly to the hothouse (âsï), where his grandmother was waiting for him. He told the old woman he must be alone that night, so she got up and went into the house where the others were.

At early daybreak she came again to the hothouse and looked in, and there she saw an immense uktena that filled the âsï, with horns on its head, but still with two human legs instead of a snake tail. It was all that was left of her boy. He spoke to her and told her to leave him, and she went away again from the door. When the sun was well up, the uktena began slowly to crawl out, but it was full noon before it was all out of the âsï. It made a terrible hissing noise as it came out, and all the people ran from it. It crawled on through the settlement, leaving a broad trail in the ground behind it, until it came to a deep bend in the river, where it plunged in and went under the water.

The grandmother grieved much for her boy, until the others of the family got angry and told her that as she thought so much of him she ought to go and stay with him. So she left them and went along the trail made by the uktena to the river and walked directly into the water and disappeared. Once after that a man fishing near the place saw her sitting on a large rock in the river, looking just as she had always looked, but as soon as she caught sight of him she jumped into the water and was gone.

Out of the Indian approach to life there came a great freedom, an intense and absorbing respect for life, enriching faith in a Supreme Power, and principles of truth, honesty, generosity, equity, and brotherhood as a guide to mundane relations.

- Black Elk, Oglala Lakota Sioux (1863-1950)

The Snake Man

Two hunters, both for some reason under a tabu against the meat of a squirrel or turkey, had gone into the woods together. When evening came they found a good camping place and lighted a fire to prepare their supper. One of them had killed several squirrels during the day, and now got ready to broil them over the fire. His companion warned him that if he broke the tabu and ate squirrel meat he would become a snake, but the other laughed and said that was only a conjurer's story. He went on with his preparation, and when the squirrels were roasted made his supper of them and then lay down beside the fire to sleep.

Late that night his companion was aroused by groaning, and on looking around he found the other lying on the ground rolling and twisting in agony, and with the lower part of his body already changed to the body and tail of a large water snake. The man was still able to speak and called loudly for help, but his companion could do nothing, but only sit by and try to comfort him while he watched the arms sink into the body and the skin take on a scaly change that mounted gradually toward the neck, until at last even the head was a serpent's head and the great snake crawled away from the fire and down the bank into the river.

The Rattlesnake's Vengeance

One day in the old times when we could still talk with other creatures, while some children were playing about the house, their mother inside heard them scream. Running out she found that a rattlesnake had crawled from the grass, and taking up a stick she killed it. The father was out hunting in the mountains, and that evening when coming home after dark through the gap he heard a strange wailing sound. Looking about he found that he had come into the midst of a whole company of rattlesnakes, which all had their mouths open and seemed to be crying. He asked them the reason of their trouble, and they told him that his own wife had that day killed their chief, the Yellow Rattlesnake, and they were just now about to send the Black Rattlesnake to take revenge.

The hunter said he was very sorry, but they told him that if he spoke the truth he must be ready to make satisfaction and give his wife as a sacrifice for the life of their chief. Not knowing what might happen otherwise, he consented. They then told him that the Black Rattlesnake would go home with him and coil up just outside the door in the dark. He must go inside, where he would find his wife awaiting him, and ask her to get him a drink of fresh water from the spring. That was all.

He went home and knew that the Black Rattlesnake was following. It was night when he arrived and very dark, but he found his wife waiting with his supper ready. He sat down and asked for a drink of water. She handed him a gourd full from the jar, but he said he wanted it fresh from the spring, so she took a bowl and went out of the door. The next moment he beard a cry, and going out he found that the Black Rattlesnake had bitten her and that she was already dying. He stayed with her until she was dead, when the Black Rattlesnake came out from the grass again and said his tribe was now satisfied.

He then taught the hunter a prayer song, and said, "When you meet any of us hereafter sing this song and we will not hurt you; but if by accident one of us should bite one of your people then sing this song over him and he will recover." And the Cherokee have kept the song to this day.

The Katydid's Warning

Two hunters camping in the woods were preparing supper one night when a Katydid began singing near them. One of them said sneeringly, "*Kû!* It sings and don't know that it will die before the season ends." The Katydid answered: "*Kû! niwï* (onomatope); O, so you say; but you need not boast. You will die before to-morrow night." The next day they were surprised by the enemy and the hunter who had sneered at the Katydid was killed.

The Bride from the South

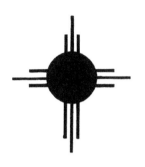

The North went traveling, and after going far and meeting many different tribes he finally fell in love with the daughter of the South and wanted to marry her. The girl was willing, but her parents objected and said, "Ever since you came the weather has been cold, and if you stay here we may all freeze to death." The North pleaded hard, and said that if they would let him have their daughter he would take her back to his own country, so at last they consented. They were married and he took his bride to his own country, and when she arrived there she found the people all living in ice houses.

The next day, when the sun rose, the houses began to leak, and as it climbed higher they began to melt, and it grew warmer and warmer, until finally the people came to the young husband and told him he must send his wife home again, or the weather would get so warm that the whole settlement would be melted. He loved his wife and so held out as long as he could, but as the sun grew hotter the people were more urgent, and at last he had to send her home to her parents.

The people said that as she had been born in the South, and nourished all her life upon food that grew in the same climate, her whole nature was warm and unfit for the North.

The Ice Man

Once when the people were burning the woods in the fall the blaze set fire to a poplar tree, which continued to burn until the fire went down into the roots and burned a great hole in the ground. It burned and burned, and the hole grew constantly larger, until the people became frightened and were afraid it would burn the whole world. They tried to put out the fire, but it had gone too deep, and they did not know what to do.

At last some one said there was a man living in a house of ice far in the north who could put out the fire, so messengers were sent, and after traveling a long distance they came to the ice house and found the Ice Man at home. He was a little fellow with long hair hanging down to the ground in two plaits. The messengers told him their errand and he at once said, "O yes, I can help you," and began to unplait his hair. When it was all unbraided he took it up in one band and struck it once across his other hand, and the messengers felt a wind blow against their cheeks. A second time he struck his hair across his hand, and a light rain began to fall. The third time he struck his hair across his open hand there was sleet mixed with the raindrops, and when he struck the fourth time great hailstones fell upon the ground, as if they had come out from the ends of his hair. "Go back now," said the lee Man, "and I shall be there to-morrow." So the messengers returned to their people, whom they found still gathered helplessly about the great burning pit.

The next-day while they were all watching about the fire there came a wind from the north, and they were afraid, for they knew that it came from the lee Man. But the wind only made the fire blaze up higher. Then a light rain began to fall, but the drops seemed only to make the fire hotter. Then the shower turned to a heavy rain, with sleet and hail that killed the blaze and made clouds of smoke and steam rise from the red coals. The people fled to their homes for shelter, and the storm rose to a whirlwind that drove the rain into every burning crevice and piled great hailstones over the embers, until the fire was dead and even the smoke ceased. When at last it was all over and the people returned they found a lake where the burning pit had been, and from below the water came a sound as of embers still crackling.

The Hunter and Selu

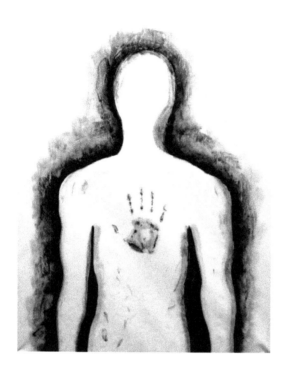

A hunter had been tramping over the mountains all day long without finding any game and when the sun went down, he built a fire in a hollow stump, swallowed a few mouthfuls of corn gruel and lay down to sleep, tired out and completely discouraged. About the middle of the night he dreamed and seemed to hear the sound of beautiful singing, which continued until near daybreak and then appeared to die away into the upper air.

All next day he hunted with the same poor success, and at night made his lonely camp again, in the woods. He slept and the strange dream came to him again, but so vividly that it seemed to him like an actual happening. Rousing himself before daylight, he still heard the song, and feeling sure now that it was real, he went in the direction of the sound and found that it came from a single green stalk of corn (*selu*). The plant spoke to him, and told him to cut off some of its roots and take them to his home in the settlement, and the next morning to chew them and "go to water" before anyone else was awake, and then to go out again into the woods, and he would kill many deer and from that time on would always be successful in the hunt. The corn plant continued to talk, teaching

him hunting secrets and telling him always to be generous with the
game he took, until it was noon and the sun was high, when it
suddenly took the form of a woman and rose gracefully into the air
and was gone from sight, leaving the hunter alone in the woods.

He returned home and told his story, and all the people knew that
he had seen Selu, the wife of Kana'tï. He did as the spirit had
directed, and from that time was noted as the most successful of all
the hunters in the settlement.

Origin of the Bear:
The Bear Songs
(Cherokee Legend)

Long ago there was a Cherokee clan called the Ani'-Tsâ'gûhï, and in one family of this clan was a boy who used to leave home and be gone all day in the mountains. After a while he went oftener and stayed longer, until at last he would not eat in the house at all, but started off at daybreak and did not come back until night. His parents scolded, but that did no good, and the boy, still went every day until they noticed that long brown hair was beginning to grow out all over his body. Then they wondered and asked him why it was that he wanted to be so much in the woods that he would not even eat at home. Said the boy, "I find plenty to eat there, and it is better than the corn and beans we have in the settlements, and pretty soon I am going into the woods to stay all the time." His parents were worried and begged him not to leave them, but he said, "It is better there than here, and you see I am beginning to be different already, so that I can not live here any longer. If you will come with me, there is plenty for all of us and you will never have to work for it; but if you want to come you must first fast seven days."

The father and mother talked it over and then told the headmen of the clan. They held a council about the matter and after everything had been said they decided: "Here we must work hard and have not always enough. There he says there is always plenty without work. We will go with him." So they fasted seven days, and on the seventh morning all the Ani'-Tsâ'gûhï left the settlement and started for the mountains as the boy led the way.

When the people of the other towns heard of it they were very sorry and sent their headmen to persuade the Ani'-Tsâ'gûhï to stay at home and not go into the woods to live. The messengers found

them already on the way, and were surprised to notice that their
bodies were beginning to be covered with hair like that of animals,
because for seven days they had not taken human food and their
nature was changing. The Ani'-Tsâ'gûhï would not come back, but
said, "We are going where there is always plenty to eat. Hereafter
we shall be called *yânû* (bears), and when you yourselves are
hungry come into the woods and call us and we shall come to give
you our own flesh. You need not be afraid to kill us, for we shall
live always." Then they taught the messengers the songs with
which to call them, and the bear hunters have these songs still.
When they had finished the songs the Ani'-Tsâ'gûhï started on
again and the messengers turned back to the settlements, but after
going a little way they looked back and saw a drove of bears going
into the woods.

First Bear Song

He-e! Ani'-Tsâ'gûhï, Ani'-Tsâ'gûhï, akwandu'li e'lanti' ginûn'ti,
*   Ani'-Tsâ'gûhï, Ani'-Tsâ'gûhï, akwandu'li e'lanti' ginûn'ti--Yû!*

He-e! The Ani'-Tsâ'gûhï, the Ani'-Tsâ'gûhï, I want to lay them low
on the ground,
    The Ani'-Tsâ'gûhï, the Ani'-Tsâ'gûhï, I want to lay them low
on the ground,--Yû!

The bear hunter starts out each morning fasting and does not eat
until near evening. He sings this song as he leaves camp, and again
the next morning, but never twice the same day.

*   *   *   *   *   *   *

Second Bear Song

This song also is sung by the bear hunter, in order to attract the bears, while on his way from the camp to the place where he expects to hunt during the day. The melody is simple and plaintive.

He-e! Hayuya'haniwä', hayuya'haniwä', hayuya'haniwä', hayuya'haniwä',
   Tsistuyi' nehandu'yanû', Tsistuyi' nehandu'yanû'--Yoho-o!
He-e! Hayuya'haniwä', hayuya'haniwä', hayuya'haniwä', hayuya'haniwä',
   Kuwâhi' nehandu'yanû', Kuwâhi' nehandu'yanû',--Yoho-o!
He-e! Hayuya'haniwä', hayuya'haniwä', hayuya'haniwä', hayuya'haniwä',
   Uyâhye' nehandu'yanû', Uyâhye' nehandu'yanû',--Yoho-o!
He-e! Hayuya'haniwä', hayuya'haniwä', hayuya'haniwä', hayuya'haniwä',
   Gâte'gwâ' nehandu'yanû', Gâte'gwâ' nehandu'yanû',--Yoho-o!
   (Recited) Ûlë-`nû' asëhï' tadeyâ'statakûhï' gûñ'näge astû' tsïkï'

He! Hayuya'haniwä' (four times),
   In Tsistu'yï you were conceived (two times)--Yoho!
He! Hayuya'haniwä' (four times),
   In Kuwâ'hï you were conceived (two times)--Yoho!
He! Hayuya'haniwä' (four times),
   In Uyâ'hye you were conceived (two times)--Yoho!
He! Hayuya'haniwä' (four times),
   In Gâte'gwâ you were conceived (two times)--Yoho!
And now surely we and the good black things, the best of all, shall see each other.

The Bear Man
(Cherokee Legend)

One springtime morning a Cherokee named Whirlwind told his wife goodbye and left his village to go up in the Smoky Mountains to hunt for wild game. In the forest he saw a black bear and wounded it with an arrow. The bear turned and started to run away, but the hunter followed, shooting one arrow after another into the animal without bringing it down. Whirlwind did not know that this bear possessed secret powers, and could talk and read the thoughts of people.

At last the black bear stopped and pulled the arrows out of his body and gave them to Whirlwind. "It is of no use for you to shoot at me," he said. "You can't kill me. Come with me and I will show you how bears live."

"This bear may kill me," Whirlwind said to himself, but the bear read his thoughts and said, "No, I will not hurt you."

"How can I get anything to eat if I go with this bear," Whirlwind thought, and again the bear knew what the hunter was thinking, and said, "I have plenty of food."

Whirlwind decided to go with the bear. They walked until they came to a cave in the side of a mountain, and the bear said, "This is not where I live, but we are holding a council here and you can see what we do." They entered the cave, which widened as they went farther in until it was as large as a Cherokee long house. It was filled with bears, old and young, brown and black, and one large white bear, who was the chief. Whirlwind sat down in a corner beside the black bear who had brought him inside, but soon the other bears scented his presence.

"What is that bad smell of a man?" one asked, but the bear chief answered, "Don't talk so. It is only a stranger come to see us. Let him alone."

The bears began to talk among themselves, and Whirlwind was astonished that he could understand what they were saying. They were discussing the scarcity of food of all kinds in the mountains, and were trying to decide what to do about it. They had sent messengers in all directions, and two of them had returned to report on what they had found. In a valley to the south, they said, was a large stand of chestnuts and oaks, and the ground beneath them was covered with mast. Pleased at this news, a huge black bear named Long Hams announced he would lead them in a dance.

While they were dancing, the bears noticed Whirlwind's bow and arrows, and Long Hams stopped and said, "This is what men use to kill us. Let us see if we can use them. Maybe we can fight them with their own weapons."

Long Hams took the bow and arrows from Whirlwind. He fitted an arrow and drew back the sinew string, but when he let go, the string caught in his long claws and the arrow fell to the ground. He saw that he could not use the bow and arrows and gave them back to Whirlwind. By this time, the bears had finished their dance, and were leaving the cave to go to their separate homes.

Whirlwind went out with the black bear who had brought him there, and after a long walk they came to a smaller cave in the side of the mountain. "This is where I live," the bear said, and led the way inside. Whirlwind could see no food anywhere in the cave, and wondered how he was going to get something to satisfy his hunger. Reading his thoughts, the bear sat up on his hind legs and made a movement with his forepaws. When he held his paws out to Whirlwind they were filled with chestnuts. He repeated this magic and his paws were filled with huckleberries which he gave to Whirlwind. He then presented him with blackberries, and finally some acorns.

"I cannot eat acorns," Whirlwind said. "Besides, you have given me enough to eat already."

For many moons, through the summer and winter, Whirlwind lived in the cave with the bear. After a while he noticed that his hair was growing all over his body like that of a bear. He learned to eat acorns and act like a bear, but he still walked upright like a man.

On the first warm day of spring the bear told Whirlwind that he had dreamed of the Cherokee village down in the valley. In the dream he heard the Cherokees talking of a big hunt in the mountains.

"Is my wife still waiting there for me?" Whirlwind asked.

"She awaits your return," the bear replied. "But you have become a bear man. If you return you must shut yourself out of sight of your people for seven days without food or drink. At the end of that time you will become like a man again."

A few days later a party of Cherokee hunters came up into the mountains. The black bear and Whirlwind hid themselves in the cave, but the hunters' dogs found the entrance and began to bark furiously.

"I have lost my power against arrows," the bear said. "Your people will kill me and take my skin from me, but they will not harm you. They will take you home with them. Remember what I told you, if you wish to lose your bear nature and become a man again." The Cherokee hunters began throwing lighted pine knots inside the cave.

"They will kill me and drag me outside and cut me in pieces," the bear said. "Afterwards you must cover my blood with leaves. When they are taking you away, if you look back you will see something."

As the bear had foretold, the hunters killed him with arrows and dragged his body outside and took the skin from it and cut the meat into quarters to carry back to their village. Fearing that they might mistake him for another bear, Whirlwind remained in the cave, but the dogs continued barking at him. When the hunters looked inside, they saw a hairy man standing upright, and one of them recognized Whirlwind.

Believing that he had been a prisoner of the bear, they asked him if he would like to go home with them and try to rid himself of his bear nature. Whirlwind replied that he would go with them, but explained that he would have to stay alone in a house for seven days without food or water in order to become as a man again.

While the hunters were loading the meat on their backs, Whirlwind piled leaves over the place where they had killed the bear, carefully covering the drops of blood. After they had walked a short distance down the mountain, Whirlwind looked behind him. He saw a bear rise up out of the leaves, shake himself, and go back into the cave.

When the hunters reached their village, they took Whirlwind to an empty house, and obeying his wishes, barred the entrance door. Although he asked them to say nothing to anyone of his hairiness and his bear nature, one of the hunters must have told of his presence in the village because the very next morning Whirlwind's wife heard that he was there.

She hurried to see the hunters and begged them to let her see her long missing husband.

"You must wait for seven days," the hunters told her. "Come back after seven days, and Whirlwind will return to you as he was when he left the village twelve moons ago."

Bitterly disappointed, the woman went away, but she returned to the hunters each day, pleading with them to let her see her husband. She begged so hard that on the fifth day they took her to the house, unfastened the door, and told Whirlwind to come outside and let his wife see him.

Although he was still hairy and walked like a bear on hind legs, Whirlwind's wife was so pleased to see him again that she insisted he come home with her. Whirlwind went with her, but a few days later he died, and the Cherokees knew that the bears had claimed him because he still had a bear's nature and could not live like a man. If they had kept him shut up in the house without food until the end of the seven days he would have become like a man again. And that is why in that village on the first warm and misty nights of springtime, the ghosts of two bears -- one walking on all fours, the other walking upright -- are still seen to this day.

The Haunted Whirlpool
(*Cherokee*)

At the mouth of Suck creek, on the Tennessee, about 8 miles below Chattanooga, is a series of dangerous whirlpools, known as "The Suck," and noted among the Cherokee as the place where Ûñtsaiyĭ', the gambler, lived long ago. They call it Ûñ'tiguhĭ', "Pot-in-the-water," on account of the appearance of the surging, tumbling water, suggesting a boiling pot. They assert that in the old times the whirlpools were intermittent in character, and the canoemen attempting to pass the spot used to hug the bank, keeping constantly on the alert for signs of a coming eruption, and when they saw the water begin to revolve more rapidly would stop and wait until it became quiet again before attempting to proceed.

It happened once that two men, going down the river in a canoe, as they came near this place saw the water circling rapidly ahead of them. They pulled up to the bank to wait until it became smooth again, but the whirlpool seemed to approach with wider and wider circles, until they were drawn into the vortex. They were thrown out of the canoe and carried down under the water, where one man was seized by a great fish and was never seen again. The other was taken round and round down to the very lowest center of the whirlpool, when another circle caught him and bore him outward and upward until he was finally thrown up again to the surface and floated out into the shallow water, whence he made his escape to shore. He told afterwards that when he reached the narrowest circle of the maelstrom the water seemed to open below him and he could look down as through the roof beams of a house, and there on the bottom of the river he had seen a great company of people, who looked up and beckoned to him to join them, but as they put up their hands to seize him the swift current caught him and took him out of their reach.

The Man in the Stump

A man who had a field of growing corn went out one day to see how it was ripening and climbed a tall stump to get a better view. The stump was hollow and a bear had a nest of cubs in the bottom. The man slipped and fell down upon the cubs, which set up such a squealing that the old she-bear heard them and came climbing down into the stump tail first, in bear fashion, to see what was the matter. The man caught hold of her by the hind legs and the old bear was so frightened that she at once climbed out again, dragging the man, who thus got out of the stump, when the bear ran away.

The Mother Bear's Song

A hunter in the woods one day heard singing in a cave. He came near and peeped in, and it was a mother bear singing to her cubs and telling them what to do when the hunters came after them.

Said the mother bear to the cubs, "When you hear the hunters coming down the creek, then-

> *Tsâ'gï, tsâ'gï, hwï'lahï';*
> *Tsâ'gï, tsâ'gï, hwï'lahï.*
> Upstream, upstream, you (must) go;
> Upstream, upstream, you (must) go.

But if you hear them coming up the creek, children, then--

> *Ge'i, ge'i, hwï'lahï';*
> *Ge'i, ge'i, hwï'lahï';*
> Downstream, downstream, you (must) go;
> Downstream, downstream, you (must) go."

*   *   *   *   *   *   *

Another hunter out in the woods one day thought he heard a woman singing to a baby. He followed the sound up to the head of the branch until he came to a cave under the bushes, and inside was a mother bear rocking her cub in her paws and singing to it this baby song, which the Ani'-Tsâ'gûhï used to know before they were turned into bears:

> *Ha'-mama', ha'-mama', ha'-mama', ha'-mama';*
> *Udâ'hale'yï hi'lûññû, hi'lûññû;*

Udâ'hale'yï hi'lûñnû, hi'lûñnû.
Let me carry you on my back (four times);
On the sunny side go to sleep, go to sleep;
On the sunny side go to sleep, go to sleep.

Baby Song, to Please the Children

Ha'wiye'-hyuwe', Ha'wiye'-hyuwe',
Yu'wê-yuwëhe', Ha'wiyëhyu'-uwe'--
Yâ'nû une'guhi' tsana'sehâ';
E`tï une'guhi' tsana'sehâ;
Yâ'nû nudûñnelû' tsa'nadiskâ

Ha'wiye'-hyuwe', Ha'wiye'-hyuwe',
Yu'wê-yuwëhe', Ha'wiyëhyu'-uwe'--
The Bear is very bad, so they say;
Long time ago he was very bad, so they say;
The Bear did so and so, they say.

The Raven Mocker
(Cherokee)

Of all the Cherokee wizards or witches the most dreaded is the Raven Mocker (*Kâ'lanû Ahkyeli'skï*), the one that robs the dying man of life. They are of either sex and there is no sure way to know one, though they usually look withered and old, because they have added so many lives to their own.

At night, when some one is sick or dying in the settlement, the Raven Mocker goes to the place to take the life. He flies through the air in fiery shape, with arms outstretched like wings, and sparks trailing behind, and a rushing sound like the noise of a strong wind. Every little while as he flies he makes a cry like the cry of a raven when it "dives" in the air--not like the common raven cry--and those who hear are afraid, because they know that some man's life will soon go out. When the Raven Mocker comes to the house he finds others of his kind waiting there, and unless there is a doctor on guard who knows bow to drive them away they go inside, all invisible, and frighten and torment the sick man until they kill him. Sometimes to do this they even lift him from the bed and throw him on the floor, but his friends who are with him think he is only struggling for breath.

After the witches kill him they take out his heart and eat it, and so add to their own lives as many days or years as they have taken from his. No one in the room can see them, and there is no sear where they take out the heart, but yet there is no heart left in the body. Only one who has the right medicine can recognize a Raven Mocker, and if such a man stays in the room with the sick person these witches are afraid to come in, and retreat as soon as they see him, because when one of them is recognized in his right shape he must die within seven days. There was once a man named Gûñskäli'skï, who had this medicine and used to hunt for Raven Mockers, and killed several. When the friends of a dying person know that there is no more hope they always try to have one of these medicine men stay in the house and watch the body until it is buried, because after burial the witches do not steal the heart.

The other witches are jealous of the Raven Mockers and afraid to come into the same house with one. Once a man who had the witch medicine was watching by a sick man and saw these other witches outside trying to get in. All at once they heard a Raven Mocker cry overhead and the others scattered "like a flock of pigeons when the hawk swoops." When at last a Raven Mocker dies these other witches sometimes take revenge by digging up the body and abusing it.

The following is told on the reservation as an actual happening:

A young man had been out on a hunting trip and was on his way home when night came on while he was still a long distance from the settlement. He knew of a house not far off the trail where an old man and his wife lived, so he turned in that direction to look for a place to sleep until morning. When he got to the house there was nobody in it. He looked into the âsï and found no one there either. He thought maybe they had gone after water, and so stretched himself out in the farther corner to sleep. Very soon he heard a raven cry outside, and in a little while afterwards the old man came into the âsï and sat down by the fire without noticing the young man, who kept still in the dark corner. Soon there was another raven cry outside, and the old man said to himself, "Now my wife is coming," and sure enough in a little while the old woman came in and sat down by her husband. Then the young man knew they were Raven Mockers and he was frightened and kept very quiet.

Said the old man to his wife, "Well, what luck did you have?" "None," said the old woman, "there were too many doctors watching. What luck did you have?" "I got what I went for," said the old man, "there is no reason to fail, but you never have luck. Take this and cook it and lees have something to eat." She fixed the fire and then the young man smelled meat roasting and thought it smelled sweeter than any meat he had ever tasted. He peeped out from one eye, and it looked like a man's heart roasting on a stick.

Suddenly the old woman said to her husband, "Who is over in the corner?" "Nobody," said the old man. "Yes, there is," said the old woman, "I hear him snoring," and she stirred the fire until it blazed and lighted up the whole place, and there was the young man lying in the corner. He kept quiet and pretended to be asleep. The old man made a noise at the fire to wake him, but still he pretended to sleep. Then the old man came over and shook him, and he sat up and rubbed his eyes as if he had been asleep all the time.

Now it was near daylight and the old woman was out in the other house getting breakfast ready, but the hunter could hear her crying to herself. "Why is your wife crying?" he asked the old man. "Oh, she has lost some of her friends lately and feels lonesome," said her husband; but the young man knew that she was crying because he had heard them talking.

When they came out to breakfast the old man put a bowl of corn mush before him and said, "This is all we have--we have had no meat for a long time." After breakfast the young man started on again, but when he had gone a little way the old man ran after him with a fine piece of beadwork and gave it to him, saying, "Take this, and don't tell anybody what you heard last, night, because my wife and I are always quarreling that way." The young man took the piece, but when he came to the first creek he threw it into the water and then went on to the settlement. There he told the whole story, and a party of warriors started back with him to kill the Raven Mockers. When they reached the place it was seven days after the first night. They found the old man and his wife lying dead in the house, so they set fire to it and burned it and the witches together.

Sun Sister and Moon Brother
(Inuit)
(ESKIMO: Boas, *Report of the Bureau of American Ethnology*, vi, 597)

In olden times a brother and his sister lived in a large village in which there was a singing house, and every night the sister with her playfellows enjoyed themselves in this house. Once upon a time, when all the lamps in the singing house were extinguished, somebody came in and outraged her. She was unable to recognize him; but she blackened her hands with soot and when the same again happened besmeared the man's back with it. When the lamps were re-lighted she saw that the violator was her brother. In great anger she sharpened a knife and cut off her breasts, which she offered to him, saying: "Since you seem to relish me, eat this." Her brother fell into a passion and she fled from him, running about the room. She seized a piece of wood (with which the lamps are kept in order) which was burning brightly and rushed out of the house. The brother took another one, but in his pursuit he fell down and extinguished his light, which continued to glow only faintly. Gradually both were lifted up and continued their course in the sky, the sister being transformed into the sun, the brother into the moon. Whenever the new moon first appears she sings:

Aningaga tapika, takirn tapika qaumidjatedlirpoq;
qaumatitaudle.
Aningaga tapika, tikipoq tapika.

(My brother up there, the moon up there begins to
shine; he will be bright.
My brother up there, he is coming up there.)

Determination of the Seasons (*Tahltan*)
(TAHLTAN: Teit, .Journal of American Folk-Lore, xxxii, 226)

Once Porcupine and Beaver quarreled about the seasons.
Porcupine wanted five winter months. He held up one hand and
showed his five fingers. He said, Let the winter months be the
same in number as the fingers on my hand." Beaver said, "No,"
and held up his tail, which had many cracks or scratches on it. He
said, "Let the winter months be the same in number as the
scratches on my tail." Now they quarreled and argued. Porcupine
got angry and bit off his thumb. Then, holding up his hand with the
four fingers, he said emphatically, "There must be only four winter
months." Beaver became a little afraid, and gave in. *For this
reason porcupines have four claws on each foot now.*

Since Porcupine won, the winter remained four months in length,
until later Raven changed it a little. Raven considered what
Porcupine and Beaver had said about the winters, and decided that
Porcupine had done right. He said, "Porcupine was right. If the
winters were made too long, people could not live. *Henceforth the
winters will be about this length,* but they will be variable. I will
tell you of the *gaxewisa* month, when people will meet together
and talk. At that time of the year people will ask questions (or
propound riddles), and others will answer. If the riddle is answered
correctly, then the person who propounded it must answer, "Fool-

hen." Raven chose this word because the fool-hen has a shorter beak than any other game bird. "If people guess riddles correctly at this time of year, then the winter will be short, and the spring come early."

# of Night and Day
(Iroquois)
(IROQUOIS: Smith, *Report of the Bureau of American Ethnology*, ii, 80)

Once upon a time the porcupine was appointed to be the leader of all the animals. Soon after his appointment he called them and presented the question, "Shall we have night and darkness, or daylight with its sunshine?"

This was a very important question, and a violent discussion arose, some wishing for daylight and the sun to rule, and others for continual night.

The chipmunk wished for night and day, weeks and months, and night to be separate from the day, so he began singing, "The light will come; we must have light," which he continued to repeat. Meanwhile the bear began singing, "Night is best; we must have darkness."

While the chipmunk was singing, the day began to dawn. Then the other party saw that the chipmunk was prevailing, and were very angry; and their leader, the bear, pursued the chipmunk, who managed to escape uninjured, the huge paw of the bear simply grazing his back as he entered his hole in a hollow tree, leaving its

black imprint, which the chipmunk has ever since retained. But night and day have ever continued to alternate.

The Theft of Fire
(*Maidu*)
(MAIDU: Dixon, *Bulletin of the American Museum of Natural History*, **xvii, 65, No. 5)**

At one time the people had found fire, and were going to use it; but Thunder wanted to take it away from them, as he desired to be the only one who should have fire. He thought that if he could do this, he would be able to kill all the people. After a time he succeeded, and carried the fire home with him, far to the south. He put Woswosim (a small bird) to guard the fire, and see that no one should steal it. Thunder thought that people would die after he had stolen their fire, for they would not be able to cook their food; but the people managed to get along. They ate most of their food raw, and sometimes got Toyeskom (another small bird) to look for a long time at a piece of meat; and as he had a red eye, this after a long time would cook the meat almost as well as a fire. Only the chiefs had their food cooked in this way. All the people lived together in a big sweat-house. The house was as big as a mountain.

Among the people was Lizard and his brother; and they were always the first in the morning to go outside and sun themselves on the roof of the sweat-house. One morning as they lay there sunning themselves, they looked west, toward the Coast Range, and saw smoke. They called to all the other people, saying that they had seen smoke far away to the west. The people, however, would not believe them, and Coyote came out, and threw a lot of dirt and dust over the two. One of the people did not like this. He said to Coyote, " Why do you trouble people? Why don't you let others alone? Why don't you behave? You are always the first to start a quarrel. You always want to kill people without any reason." Then the other people felt sorry. They asked the two Lizards about what they had seen, and asked them to point out the smoke. The Lizards did so, and all could see the- thin column rising up far to the west. One person said, "How shall we get that fire back? How shall we get it away from Thunder? He is a bad man. I don't know whether we had better try to get it or not." Then the chief said, "The best one among you had better try to get it. Even if Thunder is a bad man, we must try to get the fire. When we get there, I don't know how we shall get in but the one who is the best, who thinks he can get in, let him try." Mouse, Deer, Dog, and Coyote were the ones who were to try, but all the other people went too. They took a flute with them for they meant to put the fire in it.

They traveled a long time, and finally reached the place where the fire was. They were within a little distance of Thunder's house, when they all stopped to see what they would do. Woswosim, who was supposed to guard the fire in the house, began to sing, "I am the man who never sleeps. I am the man who never sleeps." Thunder had paid him for his work in beads, and he wore them about his neck and around his waist. He sat on the top of the sweat-house, by the smoke-hole.

After a while Mouse was sent up to try and see if he could get in. He crept up slowly till he got close to Woswosim, and then saw that his eyes were shut. He was asleep, in spite of the song that he sang. When Mouse saw that the watcher was asleep, he crawled to the opening and went in. Thunder had several daughters, and they were lying there asleep. Mouse stole up quietly, and untied the waist-string of each one's apron, so that should the alarm be given, and they jump up, these aprons or skirts would fall off, and they would have to stop to fix them. This done, Mouse took the flute, filled it with fire, then crept out, and rejoined the other people who were waiting outside.

Some of the fire was taken out and put in the Dog's ear, the remainder in the flute being given to the swiftest runner to carry. Deer, however, took a little, which he carried on the hock of his leg, where to-day there is a reddish spot. For a while all went well, but when they were about half-way back, Thunder woke up, suspected that something was wrong, and asked, "What is the matter with my fire?" Then he jumped up with a roar of thunder, and his daughters were thus awakened, and also jumped up; but their aprons fell off as they did so, and they had to sit down again to put them on. After they were all ready, they went out with Thunder to give chase. They carried with them a heavy wind and a great rain and a hailstorm, so that they might put out any fire the people had. Thunder and his daughters hurried along, and soon caught up with the fugitives, and were about to catch them, when Skunk shot at Thunder and killed him. Then Skunk called out, "After this you must never try to follow and kill people. You must stay up in the sky, and be the thunder. That is what you will be." The daughters of Thunder did not follow any farther; so the people went on safely, and got home with their fire, and people have had it ever since.

Only to the white man was nature a wilderness and only to him was the land 'infested' with 'wild' animals and 'savage' people. To us it was tame, Earth was bountiful and we were surrounded with the blessings of the Great Mystery.

- Black Elk, Oglala Lakota Sioux (1863-1950)

The time will soon be here when my grandchild will long for the cry of a loon, the flash of a salmon, the whisper of spruce needles, or the screech of an eagle.

But he will not make friends with any of these creatures and when his heart aches with longing, he will curse me.

Have I done all to keep the air fresh?

Have I cared enough about the water?
Have I left the eagle to soar in freedom?
Have I done everything I could to earn my grandchild's fondness?

- Chief Dan George, Tsleil-Waututh (1899 - 1981)

How the Buffalo were Released on Earth

In the first days a powerful being named Humpback owned all the buffalo. He kept them in a corral in the mountains north of San Juan, where he lived with his young son. Not one buffalo would Humpback release for the people on earth, nor would he share any meat with those who lived near him.

Coyote decided that something should be done to release the buffalo from Humpback's corral. He called the people to a council. "Humpback will not give us any buffalo," Coyote said. "Let us all go over to his corral and make a plan to release them."

They camped in the mountains near Humpback's place, and after dark they made a careful inspection of his buffalo enclosure. The stone walls were too high to climb, and the only entrance was through the back door of Humpback's house.

After four days Coyote summoned the people to another council, and asked them to offer suggestions for releasing the buffalo. "There is no way," said one man. "To release the buffalo we must go into Humpback's house, and he is too powerful a being for us to do that."

"I have a plan," Coyote said. "For four days we have secretly watched Humpback and his young son go about their daily activities. Have you not observed that the boy does not own a pet of any kind?"

The people did not understand what this had to do with releasing the buffalo, but they knew that Coyote was a great schemer and they waited for him to explain. "I shall change myself into a killdeer," Coyote said. "In the morning when Humpback's son goes down to the spring to get water, he will find a killdeer with a broken wing. He will want this bird for a pet and will take it back into the house. Once I am in the house I can fly into the corral, and the cries of a killdeer will frighten the buffalo into a stampede. They will come charging out through Humpback's house and be released upon the earth."

The people thought this was a good plan, and the next Morning when Humpback's son came down the path to the spring he found a killdeer with a crippled wing. As Coyote had foreseen, the boy picked up the bird and carried it into the house.

"Look here," the boy cried. "This is a very good bird!"

"It is good for nothing!" Humpback shouted. "All the birds and animals and people are rascals and schemers." Above his fierce nose Humpback wore a blue mask, and through its slits his eyes glittered. His basket headdress was shaped like a cloud and was painted black with a zig-zag streak of yellow to represent lightning. Buffalo horns protruded from the sides.

"It is a very good bird," the boy repeated.

"Take it back where you found it!" roared Humpback, and his frightened son did as he was told.

As soon as the killdeer was released it returned to where the people were camped and changed back to Coyote. "I have failed," he said, "but that makes no difference. I will try again in the morning. Perhaps a small animal will be better than a bird."

The next morning when Humpback's son went to the spring, he found a small dog there, lapping at the water. The boy picked up the dog at once and hurried back into the house. "Look here!" he cried. "What a nice pet I have."

"How foolish you are, boy!" Humpback growled. "A dog is good for nothing. I'll kill it with my club."

The boy held tight to the dog, and started to run away crying.

"Oh, very well," Humpback said. "But first let me test that animal to make certain it is a dog. All animals in the world are schemers." He took a coal of fire from the hearth and brought it closer and closer to the dog's eyes until it gave three rapid barks. "It is a real dog," Humpback declared. "You may keep it in the buffalo corral, but not in the house."

This of course was exactly what Coyote wanted. As soon as darkness fell and Humpback and his son went to sleep, Coyote opened the back door of the house. Then he ran among the buffalo, barking as loud as he could. The buffalo were badly frightened because they had never before heard a dog bark. When Coyote ran nipping at their heels, they stampeded toward Humpback's house and entered the rear door. The pounding of their hooves awakened Humpback, and although he jumped out of bed and tried to stop them, the buffalo smashed down his front door and escaped.

After the last of the shaggy animals had galloped away, Humpback's son could not find his small dog. "Where is my pet?" he cried. "Where is my little dog?"

"That was no dog," Humpback said sadly. "That was Coyote the Trickster. He has turned loose all our buffalo."

Thus it was that the buffalo were released to scatter over all the earth.

*Native American Songs, Poems
and Prayers*

The song that I will sing is an old song, so old that none knows who made it. It has been handed down through generations and was taught to me when I was but a little lad. It is now my own song. It belongs to me. This is a holy song (medicine-song), and great is its power. The song tells how, as I sing, I go through the air to a holy place where Yusun (The Supreme Being) will give me power to do wonderful things. I am surrounded by little clouds, and as I go through the air I change, becoming spirit only.

- Geronimo, Apache (1829-1909)

A Prayer For Eagles

"And he will raise you up on Eagle's wings
Bear you on the breath of dawn,
Make you to shine like the sun and,
Hold you in the palm of his hand."

Hunting Songs:

Hunting Song
(*Navajo*)

    Comes the deer to my singing,
    Comes the deer to my song,
    Comes the deer to my singing.

He, the blackbird, he am I,
Bird beloved of the wild deer.
    Comes the deer to my singing.

From the Mountain Black,
From the summit,
Down the trail, coming, coming now,
    Comes the deer to my singing.

Through the blossoms,
Through the flowers, coming, coming now,
    Comes the deer to my singing.

Through the flower dew-drops,
    Coming, coming now,
    Comes the deer to my singing.

Through the pollen, flower pollen,
    Coming, coming now,
    Comes the deer to my singing.

Starting with his left fore-foot,
Stamping, turns the frightened deer,
    Comes the deer to my singing.

Quarry mine, blessed am I
In the luck of the chase.
  Comes the deer to my singing.

  Comes the deer to my singing,
  Comes the deer to my song,
  Comes the deer to my singing.

The Rising of the Buffalo Men
(from the Osage Rite of Vigil)

I rise, I rise,
I, whose tread makes the earth to
rumble.

I rise, I rise,
I, in whose thighs there is
strength.

I rise, I rise,
I, who whips his back with his tail
when in rage.

I rise, I rise,
I, in whose humped shoulder there is power.

I rise, I rise,
I, who shakes his mane when angered.

I rise, I rise,
I, whose horns are sharp and curved.

Healing Songs:

Prayer
(from the Navajo healing ceremony called Night Chant)

Tségihi,
House made of dawn.
House made of evening light.
House made of the dark cloud.
House made of male rain.
House made of dark mist.
House made of female rain.
House made of pollen.
House made of grasshoppers.
Dark cloud is at the door.
The trail out of it is dark cloud.
The zigzag lightning stands high upon it.
Male deity!
Your offering I make.
I have prepared a smoke for you.
Restore my feet for me.
Restore my legs for me.
Restore my body for me.
Restore my mind for me.
This very day take out your spell for me.
Your spell remove for me.
You have taken it away for me.
Far off it has gone.
Happily I recover.
Happily my interior becomes cool.
Happily I go forth.
My interior feeling cool, may I walk.
No longer sore, may I walk.
Impervious to pain, may I walk.

With lively feeling may I walk.
As it used to be long ago, may I walk.
Happily may I walk.
Happily, with abundant dark clouds, may I walk.
Happily, with abundant showers, may I walk.
Happily, with abundant plants, may I walk.
Happily, on a trail of pollen, may I walk.
Happily may I walk.
Being as it used to be long ago, may I walk.
May it be beautiful before me
May it be beautiful behind me.
May it be beautiful below me.
May it be beautiful above me.
With it be beautiful all around me.
In beauty it is finished.

Rain and Planting Songs:

Song in the Garden of the House of God
(from the Navajo corn-planting ritual)

Truly in the east
The white bean
And the great corn plant
Are tied with the white lightning.
Listen! rain approaches!
The voice of the bluebird is heard.
Truly in the east
The white bean
And the great squash

Are tied with the rainbow.
Listen! rain approaches!
The voice of the bluebird is heard.

From the top of the great corn-plant the water gurgles, I hear it;
Around the roots the water foams, I hear it;
Around the roots of the plants it foams, I hear it;
From their tops the water foams, I hear it.

The corn grows up. The waters of the dark clouds drop, drop.
The rain descends. The waters from the corn leaves drop, drop.
The rain descends. The waters from the plants drop, drop.
The corn grows up. The waters of the dark mists drop, drop.

Shall I cull this fruit of the great corn-plant?
Shall you break it? Shall I break it?
Shall I break it? Shall you break it?
            Shall I? Shall you?

Shall I cull this fruit of the great squash vine?
Shall you pick it up? shall I pick it up?
Shall I pick it up? Shall you pick it up?
            Shall I? Shall you?

Korosta Katzina Song
(from the Hopi corn-planting dance, with Kachinas wearing rainbow masks)

Yellow butterflies,
Over the blossoming virgin corn,
With pollen-painted faces
Chase one another in brilliant throng.

Blue butterflies,
Over the blossoming virgin beans,
With pollen-painted faces
Chase one another in brilliant streams.

Over the blossoming corn,
Over the virgin corn,
Wild bees hum;
Over the blossoming beans,
Over the virgin beans,
Wild bees hum.

Over your field of growing corn
All day shall hang the thunder-cloud;
Over your field of growing corn
All day shall come the rushing rain.

Love Songs:

You Have No Horses
(Teton Sioux)

Well, when I was courting
"Horses you have none"
To me was said.
 Therefore, over the land
I roam.

I Will Walk
(Chippewa)

I will walk into somebody's dwelling,
Into somebody's dwelling will I walk.

To thy dwelling, my dearly beloved,
Some night will I walk, will I walk.

Some night in the winter, my beloved,
To thy dwelling will I walk, will I walk.

This very night, my beloved,
To thy dwelling will I walk, will I walk.

War Songs:

From the South
(Chippewa)

From the south they come,
The birds, the warlike birds,
With sounding wings.

I wish to change myself
To the body of that swift bird.

I throw my body in the strife.

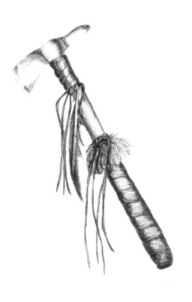

Arrow Song
(Chippewa)

Scarlet
Is its head.

Song of War
(Chippewa)

The Sioux women
pass to and fro wailing.
As they gather up their wounded men
the voice of their weeping comes back to me.

Miscellaneous Songs:

Song of the Thunders
(Chippewa dream-vision)

Sometimes I,
I go about pitying Myself
While I am carried by the wind
Across the sky.

Song to the Pleiades
(from the Pawnee Hako Ceremony)

Look as they rise, rise
Over the line where sky meets the earth;
Pleiades!
Lo! They ascending, come to guide us,
Leading us safely, keeping us one;
Pleiades,
Teach us to be, like you, united.

About the Author and Artist

Thanks for choosing this book, if you enjoyed it, please leave positive feedback.

G.W. Mullins is an Author, Photographer, and Entrepreneur of Native American / Cherokee decent. He has been a published author for over 5 years. His writing has focused on the paranormal and Native American studies. Mullins has released several books on the history/stories/fables of the Native American Indians.

Among his books are the extremely successful The Native American Story Book - Stories Of The American Indians For Children Volumes 1-5, The Native American Cookbook, and Walking With Spirits Native American Myths, Legends, And Folklore Volumes 1 Thru 6.

He has released books one and two in his Sci/fi Fantasy Series "From The Dead Of Night" series, including the Best-Selling titles - Daniel Is Waiting, and Daniel Returns.

His most recent work includes the new series Rise Of The Snow Queen Book One The Polar Bear King and Messages from The Other Side a nonfiction book about communication with the dead.

For further information, on the writing, visit G.W. Mullins' web site at http://gwmullins.wix.com/officialsite.

C.L. Hause is an Illustrator / Artist who possesses a Master Of Fine Arts Degree specializing in Studio Art. He was the winner of the 2013 Johnny Hart Memorial Award as well of several others. He has always been inspired by nature, primitive and Native American design. He has released several books of his art including "The Native American Art Book – Art Inspired By Native American Myths And Legends."

For further information, on his art, visit C.L. Hause's web site at https://clhauseart.wixsite.com/officialpage

Also Available From G.W. Mullins and C.L. Hause

Daniel Awakens A Ghost Story Begins– From The Dead Of Night
Prequel

Daniel Is Waiting A Ghost Story – From The Dead Of Night Book One

Daniel Returns A Ghost Story - From The Dead Of Night Book Two

Rise Of The Snow Queen Book One The Polar Bear King

Messages From The Other Side Stories of the Dead, Their
Communication, and Unfinished Business

Vengeance

Mysteries Of The Unseen World – Ghost, Hauntings and The
Unexplained

Haunted America Stories Of Ghost, Hauntings And The Unexplained

Timeless – A Paranormal Murder Mystery

Star People, Sky Gods, And Other Tales Of The Native American
Indians

Walking With Spirits Native American Myths, Legends, And Folklore
Volumes One Thru Six

The Native American Cookbook

Native American Cooking - An Indian Cookbook With Legends And
Folklore

The Native American Story Book - Stories Of The American Indians For
Children
Volumes One Thru Five

The Best Native American Stories For Children

Cherokee A Collection of American Indian Legends, Stories And Fables

Creation Myths - Tales Of The Native American Indians

Strange Tales Of The Native American Indians

Spirit Quest - Stories Of The Native American Indians

Animal Tales Of The Native American Indians

Medicine Man - Shamanism, Natural Healing, Remedies And Stories Of The Native American Indians

Native American Legends: Stories Of The Hopi Indians Volumes One and Two

Totem Animals Of The Native Americans

The Best Native American Myths, Legends And Folklore Volumes One Thru Three

Ghosts, Spirits And The Afterlife In Native American Indian Mythology And Folklore

War Song: Tales Of The Native American Indians

Origin Tales Of The Native American Indians

Red Road Legends Of The Native American Indians

Story Teller an Anthology of Folklore from the Native American Indians

CPSIA information can be obtained
at www.ICGtesting.com
Printed in the USA
BVHW041048050419
544725BV00017B/421/P

9 781645 709527